FEDERAL LONG-RANGE SPECTRUM PLAN

FEDERAL LONG-RANGE SPECTRUM PLAN

MATHEW B. LANE (COMPILER)

Novinka Books
New York

Senior Editors: Susan Boriotti and Donna Dennis
Coordinating Editor: Tatiana Shohov
Office Manager: Annette Hellinger
Graphics: Wanda Serrano
Editorial Production: Vladimir Klestov, Matthew Kozlowski and Maya Columbus
Circulation: Ave Maria Gonzalez, Vera Popovic, Luis Aviles, Raymond Davis,
Melissa Diaz and Jeannie Pappas
Communications and Acquisitions: Serge P. Shohov
Marketing: Cathy DeGregory

Library of Congress Cataloging-in-Publication Data

Federal long range spectrum plan / Mathew B. Lane, compiler.
   p. cm.
   Includes index.
   ISBN: 1-59033-445-0.
   1. Radiofrequency allocation—Government policy—United States. I. Lane, Mathew B.

HE8678 .F23 2002
384.54'524'0973—dc21

                                                                                                                                                     2002033840

Copyright © 2002 by Novinka Books, An Imprint of
    Nova Science Publishers, Inc.
    400 Oser Ave, Suite 1600
    Hauppauge, New York 11788-3619
    Tele. 631-231-7269   Fax 631-231-8175
    e-mail: Novascience@earthlink.net
    Web Site: http://www.novapublishers.com

All rights reserved. No part of this book may be reproduced, stored in a retrieval system or transmitted in any form or by any means: electronic, electrostatic, magnetic, tape, mechanical photocopying, recording or otherwise without permission from the publishers.

The publisher has taken reasonable care in the preparation of this book, but makes no expressed or implied warranty of any kind and assumes no responsibility for any errors or omissions. No liability is assumed for incidental or consequential damages in connection with or arising out of information contained in this book.

This publication is designed to provide accurate and authoritative information with regard to the subject matter covered herein. It is sold with the clear understanding that the publisher is not engaged in rendering legal or any other professional services. If legal or any other expert assistance is required, the services of a competent person should be sought. FROM A DECLARATION OF PARTICIPANTS JOINTLY ADOPTED BY A COMMITTEE OF THE AMERICAN BAR ASSOCIATION AND A COMMITTEE OF PUBLISHERS.

Printed in the United States of America

CONTENTS

Preface vii

Introduction ix

Chapter 1 National Policy Regarding Use of the Spectrum by Federal Departments and Agencies 1

Chapter 2 Current Federal Spectrum Use (Operational and Spectrum Requirements) 5

Chapter 3 Future Federal Operational and Spectrum Requirements 53

Chapter 4 Federal Plan for Accommodating Unsupported Requirements 61

Chapter 5 Plan for Federal Use of the Radio Frequency Spectrum 65

Chapter 6 Acronyms and Abbreviations 67

Index 73

PREFACE

Use of the radio spectrum is crucial to U.S. communications, and indeed, the national economy. In 1990, shipments of radio-communications equipment were estimated to be over $55 billion. Industries that use the spectrum, such as broadcasting and cellular telephony, also make substantial contributions to the economy, while other manufacturing and service industries use spectrum to increase their productivity. Moreover, spectrum use is essential to government functions ranging from defense and public safety to air traffic control and weather forecasting. U.S. policies for managing the spectrum must ensure that the spectrum is used efficiently and fairly while promoting innovation and serving users' needs. Protracted administrative procedures and inflexible regulation will not permit the United States to reach those goals.

Current spectrum management policies -- administered by the National Telecommunications and Information Administration (NTIA) for federal government users, and by the Federal Communications Commission (FCC) for all other users -- are under increasing strain as the demand for existing spectrum-based services grows, and new spectrum-related technologies and applications emerge. NTIA, in its role as federal spectrum manager and as the principal Executive branch adviser on telecommunications policy, prepared this report with the goal of benefiting all users of the spectrum resource.

This book details the policies and plans geared towards government oversight of the national radio spectrum, an asset we cannot afford to overlook.

INTRODUCTION

Spectrum use is an essential element of the U.S. communications infrastructure, and as such, its effective management promotes continuing U.S. economic and social development. The current system of spectrum management has been reasonably successful to date, but problems are increasingly appearing as the demands placed on the system expand rapidly. It is imperative that U.S. spectrum management ensure that the spectrum resource is used efficiently and fairly while promoting innovation and serving users' needs. Protracted administrative procedures and inflexible regulation will not permit the United States to reach those goals.

Because use of the spectrum is a vital component of many communications systems, the United States has developed strong industries based in radio-related technologies. Shipments in radio communications equipment alone are estimated to be more than $55 billion annually,[1] while revenues from broadcasting and cellular radio services, two industries built on spectrum use, are estimated to exceed $30 billion annually.[2] The United States is highly competitive in the industries related to spectrum. It is a leader in the manufacture of satellite, microwave, and cellular radio equipment, as well as in innovative uses of radio technology for purposes ranging from new forms of mobile communications and advanced military applications to garage door openers and baby monitors.

However, in light of technological and marketplace changes, the United States must evaluate whether its spectrum management policies will permit it to continue in this leadership position. Demand for spectrum is growing

---

[1] U.S. Department of Commerce, *Radio Communication and Detection Equipment* in 1991 U.S. Industrial Outlook, at 31-1 (Jan. 1991).
[2] Cellular Telecommunications Industry Association, *Data Survey* (June 1990); R. Coen, *Insider's Report #22*, McCann-Erickson (Dec. 1990).

rapidly from both the expanded use of existing services and the development of new services, such as personal communications services (PCS), satellite-based mobile services, digital audio broadcasting, and advanced television (ATV). While technical advances, the traditional means of meeting such growth in services, have been making more spectrum available, this increased supply is being overtaken by an even more rapidly increasing demand. Moreover, technology may be "pushing the envelope" of practicality, at least in the short term. How much more can technologists compress signals to permit additional use of increasingly crowded low frequencies? How useful will the higher frequencies be for inexpensive wireless communications? Accordingly, U.S. spectrum managers must ensure that their processes effectively promote, and provide strong private incentives for, efficient spectrum use. If, as many industry observers predict, the 1990s are to see the widespread deployment and strong consumer demand for mobile communications and advanced broadcasting services, the increased requirement for spectrum can only mean an increase in the challenges of managing spectrum to benefit the public. Successfully meeting these challenges in the coming decade can make a critical contribution toward enhancing the competitiveness of the U.S. economy and the quality of life of our citizens.

U.S. spectrum management has traditionally combined centralized administrative decision-making and planning with private sector investment and initiative to develop radio-based services. Central management, with the National Telecommunications and Information Administration (NTIA) managing the federal government spectrum users and the Federal Communications Commission (FCC) managing the non-federal users, has served several important functions, such as providing clear regulatory authority and a framework of consistent practices to limit radio interference among users as new applications emerge. In part, this was a response to early disputes over interference among the radio broadcasters of the 1920s -- the so-called "radio wars." By reserving spectrum for potential future uses, centralized management has also helped to shape and define the developing communications infrastructure.

Concurrently, the reliance on private sector investment has also led to considerable success. For example, when radio broadcasting first came of age in the 1920s, the United States did not establish government-owned radio stations, nor did it choose to regulate radio communication as a public utility, despite the recommendations of the first radio conference convened by then-Commerce Secretary Herbert Hoover.³ Instead, commercial broadcasters were allowed to establish themselves, and they prospered on the basis of selling paid advertising. Similarly, as technologies permitting efficient, two-way voice communications over radio spectrum developed, the United States relied on the initiative of common carriers and private radio operators to bring these services to the American public. One of the triumphs of U.S. communications policy is the successful development of a strong and independent system of privately-owned and operated radio-based services.

Those familiar with the history of spectrum management may find that the issues mentioned -- crowded spectrum, excess demand, technology placing pressures on the system -- seem familiar. Users, engineers, and politicians have struggled with similar spectrum management issues almost since the first practical application of radio, altered only by the specific context and the technology of the day. Current conditions raise questions as to whether the prevailing system of spectrum management continues to be both efficient and fair. To address such questions, in December 1989, NTIA released a *Notice of Inquiry* (the *Notice*) seeking information on key issues in spectrum use and management.⁴ In response, they received 118 initial and reply comments from more than 100 different organizations and individuals.

The extensive public response to the *Notice* is one indication that once again, the management and use of spectrum is an item of increasing national interest. Spectrum issues are moving to the foreground of communications policy debates. During the past year, spectrum use and management, a subject previously relegated to technical engineering and economics journals, found its place in major business and policy publications -- including a *Business Week* cover story, a *Wall Street Journal* editorial, and a *National Journal* feature article.⁵

In addition to the questions asked in the *Notice*, fundamental spectrum management issues are being raised throughout the federal government. The FCC has recently begun several spectrum-related proceedings that address

---

³ G.O. Robinson, *The Federal Communications Act: An Essay on Origins and Regulatory Purpose*, in A Legislative History of the Communications Act of 1934 at 9-10 (M.D. Paglin, ed. 1989) *(Robinson Essay)*.

⁴*Co mprehensive Policy Review of the Use and Management of the Radio Frequency Spectrum*, 54 Fed. Reg. 50,694 (1989) *(Notice)*.

⁵ *See, e.g., Airwave Wars,* Business Week, July 23, 1990, at 48; M.E. Kriz, *Supervising Scarcity,* The National Journal, July 7, 1990, at 1660; *Congress's Wheel of Fortune,* Wall Street Journal (editorial), July 27, 1990 at A10, col. 1; *see also* P. Huber, *Underground Networks,* Forbes, Oct. 29, 1990, at 144; *No Vacancies,* Wall Street Journal, Nov. 9, 1990, at R14; A. Sikes, *Brink of a Revolution,* Newsweek, Jan. 14, 1991 at 8.

aspects of these issues.[6] Moreover, legislative efforts are focusing national attention on managing and planning for future uses of the spectrum.[7]

NTIA, as the Executive branch telecommunications policy adviser and manager of federal government uses of the spectrum, has a strong interest in, and is well qualified to examine, these issues. In preparing this report, comments on the *Notice* provided one extremely valuable source of information for analysis. NTIA also considered both academic and technical research and FCC proceedings on spectrum issues, including proposals for new apportionment and regulatory strategies.

Considering the diversity and dynamism of the spectrum-using industries in the United States, NTIA believes that U.S. spectrum management should rely less on a centralized administrative system and more on private sector incentives to achieve national goals. Accordingly, they strongly support increased use of market mechanisms to apportion spectrum among private users, and increased flexibility to provide users with greater ability to determine for themselves how spectrum should be employed. Moreover, because of the extensive use of spectrum by the federal government as well as by the private sector, the NTIA strongly believe that the public should have increased access to the process by which they manage federal spectrum.

While NTIA strongly recommends making these fundamental reforms, they recognize that much can be accomplished in the short term through specific changes to the existing system. These changes include improving current procedures and data files, making better use of available measurement tools, establishing strategic spectrum management goals, and planning the steps needed to achieve those goals.

However, as in the past, the challenge of ensuring efficient and fair spectrum use will not be met by these "fixes" or by simply seeking to accommodate new users by moving existing users. Simply opening tracts of

---

[6] *See, e.g., Establishment of Procedures to Provide a Preference to Applicants Proposing an Allocation for New Services*, Notice of Proposed Rule Making, 5 FCC Rcd 2766 (1990) (*Pioneer's Preference*); *see also Amendment of the Commission's Rules to Establish Personal Communications Services*, Notice of Inquiry, 5 FCC Rcd 3995 (1990) (*Personal Communications Services*); *New Digital Audio Radio Services*, Notice of Inquiry, 5 FCC Rcd 5237 (1990) (*Digital Audio Broadcasting*). The Chairman of the FCC recently announced his intention to develop a spectrum reserve for new communications uses. *See* remarks of Alfred C. Sikes, Chairman, Federal Communications Commission, Before the Practicing Law Institute (Washington, D.C., Dec. 6, 1990).

[7] S. 218, the *Emerging Telecommunications Technology Act of 1991*, 102d Cong., 1st Sess. (1991) and H.R. 531, the *Emerging Telecommunications Technology Act of 1991*, 102d Cong., 1st Sess. (1991); *see also* H.R. 2965, the *Emerging Telecommunications Technology Act of 1989*, 101st Cong., 1st Sess. (1989).

spectrum for reallocation will not necessarily result in long-term efficiencies. Only basic changes in the U.S. system can achieve that goal.

MANAGING RADIO FREQUENCY SPECTRUM

NTIA serves as the President's principal advisor on telecommunication policies. On the President's behalf, NTIA also manages the radio frequency spectrum used by the Federal agencies in satisfying their missions. In this role, NTIA processes the Federal agencies' request for frequency assignments; coordinates current and future spectrum requirements among the Federal agencies; and along with the Federal Communications Commission (FCC) and the Department of State, develops and promotes the United States' positions on spectrum management issues within international treaty bodies and other fora. Because of its unique role as policy adviser and spectrum manager, NTIA must balance the spectrum interests of the Federal agencies while also advancing policies that promote the benefits of technological developments in the United States for all users of telecommunications services. As Federal spectrum manager, NTIA promotes policies to improve spectrum efficiency, to increase private sector access to scarce spectrum resources, and to plan for future Federal spectrum needs, including those critical national defense, public safety and law enforcement needs.

BACKGROUND ON THE NATIONAL SPECTRUM ALLOCATION PROCESS

In 1934, the Communications Act was signed into law establishing the respective responsibilities for spectrum management in the United States. The statute reserved to the President the authority to make radio frequencies available to all stations belonging to or operated by the United States. NTIA exercises this authority on behalf of the President ensuring that federal agencies can meet their critical communications needs, both in peace time and during emergencies, in the areas of national defense and security, air safety, maintenance and preservation of our natural resources, law enforcement, management of national disasters, exploration of space, and other Federal government services and functions. The Communications Act of 1934 also created the FCC as an independent agency with the responsibility to manage the spectrum to meet the needs of the state and local governments and the private sector.

To meet the respective needs of the private sector and federal government, the President, through NTIA and its predecessors, and the FCC over the past 68 years have divided approximately 300 GHz of usable radio spectrum into government exclusive, non-government exclusive and "shared" bands. Each of these approximately 900 bands have been allocated to one or more of 41 radio-communication services such as broadcasting, mobile, fixed, and mobile satellite.

The FCC makes domestic spectrum allocation decisions through public rulemakings. NTIA coordinates its allocation decisions in government-exclusive bands through the Interdepartment Radio Advisory Committee (IRAC), which is comprised of representatives from the major spectrum users among the Federal agencies. The FCC and NTIA coordinate on any spectrum allocation decisions involving "shared" bands. They work together every day to coordinate spectrum decisions that affect our constituencies and to ensure that the current and future needs of both the government and private sector for access to the spectrum are satisfied.

AN OVERVIEW OF SPECTRUM USE IN THE UNITED STATES

Over the years, spectrum use has expanded from the very low frequency ranges to the higher frequency ranges. Over 93 percent of all FCC licensees and Federal government frequency authorizations are in the 0 to 3 gigahertz (GHz) range. Of the spectrum below 3 GHz, 14 percent of the spectrum is Federal government exclusive, 31 percent is non-Federal government exclusive, and the remaining 55 percent is shared between the Federal government and private sector uses. Throughout the usable spectrum, NTIA has authorized the use of some 445,845 assignments for Federal government use, the protection of spectrum used by Canada and Mexico, and other frequencies specified by the FCC. NTIA processes approximately 300 to 500 Federal agency requests for frequency assignment actions daily.

The entire spectrum management process has to be flexible, dynamic, adaptable to changing requirements, and timely to meet the national needs for spectrum. The spectrum below 3 GHz is extremely congested. Thus, finding spectrum below 3 GHz for the deployment of new technologies, such as third generation wireless or ultra-wideband services, has been a complex and challenging process.

As a result of the requirements of the Omnibus Budget Reconciliation Act of 1993 and the Balanced Budget Act of 1997, NTIA has identified over 240 MHz of spectrum used either exclusively by the Federal government or shared with the private sector for reallocation to private sector uses. In 1998, Congress enacted a law that requires the private sector beneficiaries of this spectrum to reimburse Federal agencies for the costs of relocating from certain of the identified frequency bands. NTIA is now in the process of finalizing these reimbursement rules. The President's Budget for Fiscal Year 2003 contained a legislative proposal to streamline this reimbursement process by creating a fund from spectrum auction proceeds to reimburse the affected Federal agencies. The Department of Commerce expects to transmit this proposal to Congress later this spring.

OVERVIEW OF NTIA SUPPORT FOR NATIONAL DEFENSE, LAW ENFORCEMENT, AND PUBLIC SAFETY

Spectrum availability has a profound affect on national defense and Federal law enforcement and public safety agencies with respect to their ability to support their mission of homeland defense, border security, criminal investigation, counter-terrorism activities, and the general safety of the American people. To meet these needs, NTIA assigns spectrum to Federal agencies on a continuous basis. This frequency assignment system enables Federal agencies to meet their radio-communication needs under any conditions from peacetime to national emergencies.

In special cases, such as the September 11th terrorist attacks on the Pentagon and the World Trade Center, NTIA responded with a 24 hour-a-day, 7 days-a-week special frequency operation to process special requests by Federal agencies for search and rescue and associated operations at the site of these attacks, related law enforcement activities, and spectrum requirements for DOD special operations. NTIA processed emergency requests from DOD, the Departments of Justice, Treasury and Energy, the Federal Emergency Management Agency, the White House Communications Agency, and the American Red Cross. To meet DOD's special spectrum needs, NTIA expedited coordination of more than 6,700 such assignments through the use of a special computer automation process.

Of the total Federal frequency assignments, NTIA has authorized approximately 40 percent for DOD's use. The largest number of these DOD assignments, approximately 56 percent, support DOD's land, sea, and air mobile operations. Other DOD uses include fixed microwave operations (14 percent); space operations (9 percent); radiolocation and radio-navigation (5 percent); experimental operations (3 percent); and combinations of the above operations (13 percent). DOD like many Federal agencies has adopted more spectrum efficient technologies in recent years, and thus, has significantly reduced its frequency assignments. In the past five years, DOD has decreased its spectrum use by 16 percent.

NTIA also works with the Federal agencies to ensure that spectrum is available to meet the future radio-communication needs of the U.S. Government. NTIA has a spectrum certification program that enables agencies to present proposed systems for review and evaluation to see if spectrum will be available for operation of these systems in the future and to ensure that the systems meet the rules, regulations and standards that are required to prevent interference. In 2001, NTIA certified spectrum availability for 138 systems of which 57 percent were DOD systems with an approximate value of $10.1 billion. The new systems included radars, terrestrial trunking communications systems, enhanced airborne warning control system, and weapon control systems. NTIA also works closely with and has agreements with DOD's Joint Spectrum Center. They have mutually developed computer automated spectrum management tools that have been adopted by most Federal agencies to make applications for frequency assignments. Use of these tools ensures that the requests meets the NTIA rules and regulations governing spectrum use and that interference to and from others is prevented.

ACCOMMODATION OF NEW TECHNOLOGIES - THIRD GENERATION WIRELESS AND ULTRAWIDEBAND

NTIA is currently working with FCC, DOD and other Federal agencies to accommodate two new technologies that will provide new radio services to the public and the Federal government. Accommodating these technologies poses unique and difficult challenges for the spectrum management community.

Third Generation Wireless

Over the past decade, there has been a tremendous growth worldwide in the use of cellular-based wireless telecommunications systems. The Department of Commerce and NTIA believe that this global growth will continue. The "third generation" (or "3G") systems advanced by industry propose to provide mobile and satellite-based broadband capabilities. While current cellular and PCS wireless systems are expected to evolve to 3G technology over time, there is a strong desire from the wireless industry for additional spectrum now to establish 3G networks.

In recognition of this growth and the trend toward global markets for wireless services, the International Telecommunication Union (ITU) has considered the spectrum requirements for evolving 3G systems, which is internationally termed International Mobile Telecommunications-2000, or IMT-2000. At the May 2000 World Radio-communication Conference (WRC-2000) in Istanbul, Turkey, an ITU-established agenda item called for the review of spectrum and regulatory issues for advanced mobile applications in the context of IMT-2000. The ITU acknowledged the need to provide additional spectrum, particularly for the terrestrial component of IMT-2000 applications. The ITU forecasts that 160 MHz of additional spectrum would be required for 3G systems. This amount is over and above that spectrum already allocated internationally for 1- and 2G systems. The ITU identified several frequency bands that could be used for IMT-2000 systems. However, member administrations of the ITU retained the right to implement any of the bands in any time frame, for any service or technology, and could use any portion of the identified bands that they deemed appropriate to satisfy national requirements.

Since 2000, NTIA, the FCC, and the Federal agencies have been working cooperatively to take certain actions to identify spectrum for 3G services. After extensive public outreach and work with industry and affected agencies on technical analyses of the various band options, NTIA and the Federal agencies are now focusing specifically on the 1710-1770 MHz band, while the FCC is focusing on the 2110-2170 MHz band. Viability assessments on both bands will be released later this spring.

Ultrawideband

Recent advances in microcircuits and other technologies have resulted in the development of pulsed radar and communications systems with very narrow pulse widths and very wide bandwidths. These "ultrawideband" or "UWB" devices are capable of accurately locating nearby objects, seeing through objects, and communicating using multiple paths. While most of them operate at very low power levels, they operate across multiple bands of frequencies allocated to numerous other conventional radio communications technologies, including safety-of-life and other critical governmental systems.

In May of 2000, the Federal Communications Commission issued a notice of proposed rulemaking (NPRM) to amend its rules to accommodate UWB devices in the radio spectrum without causing harmful interference to governmental operations (including critical air traffic control, weather warning systems, and national defense systems) or commercial communications systems (including TV and radio broadcasting, domestic and international commercial satellites, cellular telephones). NTIA conducted extensive measurements and analysis, including tests and analysis of UWB effects on a number of governmental systems and the global positioning satellite (GPS) system. NTIA worked closely with the affected Federal agencies, including DOD, and the FCC to ensure that the FCC's rules will protect critical Government uses of the spectrum. NTIA is now in the process of coordinating the final rules, which the FCC adopted on February 14th of this year.

CONCLUSION

In summary, NTIA works closely with the Federal spectrum management community to balance the spectrum needs of the Government agencies with those of the private sector.'

Chapter 1

NATIONAL POLICY REGARDING USE OF THE SPECTRUM BY FEDERAL DEPARTMENTS AND AGENCIES

The United States is vitally dependent upon the use of the radio spectrum to carry out national policies and achieve national goals. Use of the spectrum is vital to the security and welfare of the Nation and to the conduct of its foreign affairs. This use exerts a powerful influence upon our everyday lives, in countless ways, annually contributing significantly to the Nation's growth and economy.

The radio spectrum is a limited natural resource which is accessible to all nations. It is imperative that we develop and administer our use of this resource wisely so as to maintain a free democratic society and to stimulate the healthy growth of the Nation, while ensuring its availability to serve future requirements in the best interest of the Nation. Therefore, consistent with our international treaty obligations and with due regard for the rights of other nations, the national objectives for the use of the radio spectrum are to make effective, efficient, and prudent use of the spectrum in the best interest of the Nation, with care to conserve it for uses where other means of communication are not available or feasible. Specifically, in support of national policies and the achievement of national goals, the primary objectives are:

(a) to enhance the conduct of foreign affairs;
(b) to serve the national security and defense;
(c) to safeguard life and property;
(d) to support crime prevention and law enforcement;

(e) to support the national and international transportation systems;
(f) to foster conservation of natural resources;
(g) to provide for the national and international dissemination of educational, general, and public interest information and entertainment;
(h) to make available rapid, efficient, nationwide, and worldwide radio-communication services;
(i) to promote scientific research, development, and exploration;
(j) to stimulate social and economic progress; and
(k) in summary, to improve the well being of man.

In carrying out these objectives, the Government shall, in general, encourage the development and regulate the use of radio and wire communications subject to its control so as to meet the needs of national security, safety of life and property, international relations, and the business, social, educational, and political life of the Nation.

Specifically, the Government shall:

(a) aggressively foster the development, investigation, selection, and standardization of a worldwide system of radio and electronic aids for marine navigation and communication, since the national security, the Nation's sea commerce, and the assurance of adequate safety of life and property at sea for ships of all nations require such an efficient, integrated, and standardized system.

(b) aggressively foster the development, investigation, selection, and standardization of a worldwide system of radio and electronic aids for air navigation and communication, since the national security, the Nation's air commerce, and the assurance of adequate safety of life and property in flight require such an efficient, integrated, and standardized system.

(c) promote the development and use of radio for the protection of the lives and property of its citizens and of other national resources where other means of communication are not appropriate or available.

(d) foster such research and development activities in the telecommunication field as will permit and encourage the most beneficial use of the radio spectrum in the national interest.

(e) promote the development and use of radio to improve the efficiency and economy of Government operations where other means of communication are not appropriate or available.

In the procurement of telecommunications services, the Federal Government places heavy reliance on the private sector. In order to emphasize the Government's proper role as a user, rather than a telecommunications provider, any proposal which requires the Government to perform any "provider" functions, shall be adopted only if commercial service is:

(a) not available to the user during the time needed;
(b) not adequate from either a technical or operational standpoint; or
(c) significantly more costly.

Establishment of Federal telecommunications systems is acceptable only if such an approach will result in significant savings over an otherwise acceptable commercial service offering. To be considered significant the savings must exceed 10 percent of the cost of the commercial service. The cost estimate of the non-commercial approach must include, as a minimum, all of the factors called out by Office of Management and Budget Circular A–76. If the proposed approach involves heavy investment, rapid obsolescence, or uncertain requirements, the minimum savings threshold should be increased to reflect these factors.

The Government shall establish separate communication satellite systems only when they are required to meet unique governmental needs, or are otherwise required in the national interest. Therefore, within the jurisdiction of the U.S. Government, use of the radio frequency (RF) spectrum for radio transmissions by U.S. Government stations shall be made only as authorized by the Assistant Secretary.

The Government regards the radio frequency spectrum as a world resource in the public domain; consequently, its policies ensure that this resource is used in the best interest of the Nation, but with high regard to the needs and rights of other nations. In this regard, the Government considers the International Telecommunication Union (ITU) the principal competent and appropriate international organization for the purpose of formulating international regulations on telecommunication matters, and recognizes that other international bodies, such as the International Civil Aviation Organization, Intergovernmental Maritime Consultative Organization, and the World Meteorological Organization also provide appropriate international organizations for considering specialized telecommunication matters.

In view of the limitations of the usable radio frequency spectrum, and to ensure the best possible return from the use thereof, the Government in time of peace shall require all users to: a) justify any except an emergency request for radio frequencies prior to the assignment or use of such frequencies; b) confirm periodically the justification of continued use; c) employ up-to-date spectrum conserving techniques as a matter of normal procedure; and d) assure the ability to discontinue the electronic functioning of any emission system, including satellites, when required in the interest of communication efficiency and effectiveness.

The Federal Government, in its role of leadership in the application of advanced technology, shall foster the application of spectrum-conserving methods for radio communication systems used by the Federal Government. Spectrum-conserving systems are new or existing systems that make use of innovative designs or unique applications that result in efficient use of frequency, space, and time. Efficient use is a mission-oriented factor that combines the requirements of the mission with available techniques to provide the most effective solution. Federal agencies are encouraged to use spectrum-conserving technologies and methods where they will satisfy agency operational requirements and will enhance service, economy of operation, and the more efficient and effective use of the radio spectrum. However, where spectrum is readily available due to geographic considerations or other factors, or where mission requirements mandate, security, economics, or some technical or system performance criterion may be the determining factor in system selection.

Chapter 2

CURRENT FEDERAL SPECTRUM USE (OPERATIONAL AND SPECTRUM REQUIREMENTS)

FEDERAL GOVERNMENT'S USE OF TELECOMMUNICATIONS

Telecommunications are vital to the functioning of government, whether it is local, state, or Federal. The workings of government require rapid and timely information to make informed decisions and to direct and control the governmental activities that are removed from the seat of government. The Federal Government depends on telecommunications in support of its operations in the discharging of its Constitutionally-mandated responsibilities. In its day-to-day activities, the Federal Government uses a vast array of telecommunications services, ranging from conventional wireline telephone service to secure worldwide satellite-borne data communications. The primary use of telecommunications by the Federal Government is in support of providing its services to the public.

As the U.S. population grows and migrates, Government operations tend to follow, establishing its presence in new locations throughout the Nation. Currently, more than 1 dollar out of every 10 spent on non-military telecommunications products is in support of the Federal civilian workforce, which accounts for only 2.8 percent of the total U.S. workforce. Telecommunications link together the expanding Government presence typified by the 20,000 buildings purchased by the Government since 1970, and the addition of 73,000 Federal workers. This expansion was necessary to serve the 44 million Americans added to our population since 1970.

Since 1970, Government consumption has grown by about four to five percent annually, compared to about three to four percent in the overall economy. This growth in Government is accompanied by a parallel growth in Federal Government services. Many of these services, such as law enforcement and air traffic control, depend on telecommunications for efficient accomplishment. Thus, the growth in Government services has produced increased telecommunications requirements.

The Federal Government is not, generally, a telecommunications provider, either to the public or to Government agencies. Except in those cases where commercial services are not available or otherwise suitable, telecommunications supporting Government activities are procured from the private sector. Thus, competition in the telecommunications industry impacts Government procurement of these services to at least the same degree, if not more, as that to private sector users.

Telecommunications services used by the Federal Government can be classified into two basic types: (1) those that are based on wireline systems, including those that have access to the public switched networks, and (2) those services based on spectrum-dependent radio-communication systems.

THE FEDERAL GOVERNMENT'S USE OF RADIO-COMMUNICATIONS

This section presents, in brief, the nature and scope of the Federal Government's use of radio-communications, including the dominant factors which dictate such use. The investment in spectrum-dependent equipment is in excess of $80 billion. This figure does not include the operating budgets required to support the equipment. Some 300,000 radio frequency authorizations are current for operation of Federal radio-communications systems.

At the onset it should be recognized that "use of the radio frequency spectrum" covers a range of radio-communication and electronic facilities far in excess of the "radio" of by-gone years which meant, for the public at least, primarily broadcasting and wireless communications to ships at sea. The Federal Government facilities involved include not only radio stations of many categories but a myriad of electronic devices whose uses are characterized by the term "radio-communications".

Current Federal Spectrum Use

In understanding the Federal Government's use of radio-communications, one must appreciate the interplay with non-Federal Government use of radio systems, many of which share the same radio frequency spectrum. In addition to the shared use of spectrum, there is a substantial interface between Government and non-Government radio operations. Non-Government ships, aircraft, and vehicles are served by Government radio facilities; Federal law enforcement agencies have intercommunication with their state and local government counterparts; Federal electrical power systems interconnect with non-Federal, both domestic and international; Civil Air Patrol stations communicate with the military services-- and so forth.

In general, U.S. Government radio facilities, supported by a significant research and development complex, fall in the following categories:

1. Conventional terrestrial radio-communication facilities - such as long-range high frequency (HF) circuits; radio-communication services to ships and aircraft, including air traffic control, land mobile, and microwave point-to-point communication facilities.

2. Space-based radio-communications stations - used for relay of signals, Earth observation and weather forecasting, and nuclear detonation detection.

3. Radars - used for the location of aircraft or ships, missile detection, weapons control, and weather observation.

4. Radio-navigation facilities - both terrestrial and space-based, used for determining position and as an aid in the safe navigation of ships and aircraft.

5. Telemetry - radio transmission of measured or sensed quantities or conditions of given physical properties such as hydro/meteorological or stress/strain data including the receipt of such information from spacecraft. Radio astronomy observations may be considered as a form of telemetry in the broad sense where the transmitted signals are of natural origin.

6. Various radio frequency spectrum-dependent systems - systems used for security, inventory control, position locating, remote control of mobile devices, and low-powered devices not requiring specific National Telecommunications and Information Administration (NTIA) authorization for operation.

Two dominant themes are present in the Government's use of radio:

1. Requirements for telecommunication are placed upon the Federal Agencies by virtue of the missions and programs approved by the President consistent with Congressional legislative and funding support, and

2. The use of radio rather than other forms of communications as dictated by the inescapable restrictions imposed by time, geography, and the need for mobility.

The acquisition and use of radio-communication facilities are essential to accomplish the wide variety of individual and interrelated missions of the Federal Agencies which serve the public in many ways. Further, the essentiality of the facilities themselves is established through the Government's budget and appropriation procedures pursuant to congressional approval and Presidential direction. Therefore, as long as spectrum regulatory agencies are not judgmental of the spectrum requirements, the basic management question is not whether the spectrum should be used to support these activities but how it may best be used to meet the requirements to which the agencies are committed–taking into account affected occupants of the same spectrum, present and future, national and international.

Since spectrum use has a low cost to Federal users, the use of spectrum-dependent systems as opposed to wireline systems is based on the relative cost of the equipment. As spectrum availability decreases, the economic equations may, of necessity, include an increased cost associated with spectrum use to ensure spectrum availability for those requirements that have no viable alternatives.

Increased demand for the spectrum resource, particularly by the private sector, is forcing an increased level of sharing, both among differing radio services in a common frequency band, and between Government and private-sector users. Systems using spread-spectrum modulation, and systems which operate in multiple radio services on the same frequency will become more prevalent, and present challenges for future spectrum managers.

RADIO SPECTRUM MANAGEMENT

The Communications Act of 1934 established the Federal Communications Commission (FCC) and provided the framework for telecommunications regulation within the United States. The Act, passed in 1934, succeeded the Radio Act of 1927 and established the division of authority for spectrum management between the Executive and Legislative branches of the Government, making them independent, co-equal authorities. Radio stations belonging to, and operated by the Federal Government do not come under FCC control.[1] The President's authority for assigning frequencies to Government stations, and certain other functions, were delegated to the Secretary of Commerce by Executive Order 12046 in 1977. Within the Department of Commerce, NTIA has been delegated these responsibilities, and works closely with the FCC in the regulation and planning of the radio frequency spectrum.

Radio frequency spectrum available for assignment to Federal Government stations is shown in the U.S. National Table of Frequency Allocations, and amplified by regulations contained in the *Manual of Regulations and Procedures for Federal Radio Frequency Management*. The U.S. Table is comprised of the Government Table of Frequency Allocations, and the FCC Table of Frequency Allocations as appears in Title 47, Code of Federal Regulations, Part 2. In the early 1940's, spurred by the rapid increase in Government requirements for radio systems, the FCC and the President's Interdepartment Radio Advisory Committee (IRAC) agreed to a national allocation table that contained some frequency bands allocated exclusively for Federal Government use, some exclusively for private sector use, and the rest shared between Government and non-Government users.

---

[1] Communications Act of 1934, as amended, Section 305 (a).

CURRENT USE OF RADIO SYSTEMS BY THE EXECUTIVE BRANCH AGENCIES

Use of the Radio Frequency Spectrum by the Military Services

The paramount requirement of military communications-electronics (C-E) is to provide telecommunications, navigation, and special purpose electronic systems that are responsive to the requirements of the National Command Authorities, the Joint Chiefs of Staff, the Commanders of Unified or Specified Commands, the Services, and defense agencies in the accomplishment of designated missions and functions in peacetime, contingency situations, and at all levels of conflict, including general nuclear warfare. Military C-E systems are developed and produced to perform functions that accommodate crisis management, support nuclear strategy, and meet other wartime requirements. These systems are designed to facilitate a rapid transition from peace to war as well as to satisfy peacetime needs. The nature of the systems and the functions to be performed make military tactical and strategic operations highly dependent on the usable radio frequency spectrum.

The foregoing factors demand that sound engineering and administrative practices be applied by the military services toward ensuring efficiency in the management and use of the radio frequency spectrum to support operations. Under normal peacetime conditions, military service needs are satisfied while minimizing the impact on other users through efficiently exercised management. Service needs are met so that the primary uses of the spectrum are in conformity with the National and International Radio Regulations. Other needs are met on a noninterference basis. The management of the frequency resources required to support a balanced and operationally effective training/contingency program for the military force structure requires a constant effort to refine and improve management functioning. It is only through diligent and progressive management and continued technological advancement that the radio frequency spectrum requirements, incident to national readiness and security, can be adequately met.

A short description of each of the military services' dependence on radio frequencies is presented below.

Defense Information Systems Agency (DISA)

DISA engineers, manages, and operationally directs the Defense Communications System (DCS) which provides the long-haul worldwide communications for the Department of Defense (DOD). In addition to land lines (including wire and fiber optic cables) and submarine cables, the DCS includes an extensive worldwide network of troposcatter, microwave, and HF systems, as well as the satellites and Earth terminals of the Defense Satellite Communications System (DSCS). The individual components of the DCS are provided by the Military Departments which are responsible for the operation and maintenance of the facilities. The frequency spectrum with which the DISA is concerned ranges from the lower portion of the HF band up through the extra high frequency (EHF) radio frequencies, and into laser frequencies used in the fiber optic cables.

Department of the Army

The Office of the Director of Information Systems for Command, Control, Communications, and Computer is responsible for all electronic communication, computer and information management activities for the Department of the Army. The Army Spectrum Manager, who reports directly to the Director of Information Systems for Command, Control, Communications, and Computer, is responsible for ensuring unity of effort in frequency supportability and radio regulatory matters, and for providing policy guidance on any interdepartmental or host nation issues. He and his staff address objectives, policy, radio regulatory positions and resource management within the Army, including training of frequency personnel; and, interfaces spectrum matters with other DOD and Federal agencies and with the FCC.

Additionally, frequency assignments for Army use within the Continental United States (CONUS) are made by organizations under the direction of the Army Spectrum Manager. The Communications-Electronics Service Office provides national and international level support to Army spectrum management activities including coordination of spectrum use with other government agencies, participation in national and international spectrum management forums, certification of spectrum-dependent equipment, and management of host nation agreements to support use of spectrum-dependent equipment. The Army Frequency Management Office CONUS and the Area Frequency Coordinators located at White Sands Missile Range and the Electronic Proving Grounds provide the vital link between national spectrum management and Army operations. These organizations directly respond to frequency action requests from operational tactical units, administrative support units, research and development organization, and other Army efforts.

Due to the high mobility of Army operations, the dispersal of Army units, and the wide range of Army spectrum-dependent systems, Army frequency use requires extraordinary planning. Army frequency management techniques and procedures will continue to change to support Army modernization efforts that require high data rate systems with related increases in bandwidth and real time frequency agile systems. This dynamic environment presents a unique challenge to Army frequency management offices and to those organizations with which the Army shares the radio frequency spectrum.

The trend in Army spectrum-dependent systems is towards embedded automation and signal processing techniques to improve information exchange. The emphasis in new design (e.g., software-defined radios) is to operate in a radio interfering environment, and to provide maximum tuning ranges to permit assignment flexibility in different ITU Regions and to solve local spectrum congestion problems. Experimental work continues at EHF in both equipment design and radio propagation sciences. Data transfer requirements placed upon tactical radio relay systems have increasingly driven bandwidth, interoperability and flexibility in supporting computer techniques, such as time division multiplexing and packet switching.

Training at individual and unit levels has increased radio spectrum requirements for communications, weapons systems, and countermeasure tactical systems. The Fort Irwin, California, and Fort Polk, Louisiana, National Training Centers (NTC) are instrumented for unit testing. Army forces are rotated through the NTCs as part of the annual testing and evaluation of training. The Army is reviewing its frequency management process to achieve the highest utilization and training capability while limiting potential interference.

Army aviation operates in the National Airspace with installed air navigation and radar systems, very high frequency (VHF) or ultra high frequency (UHF) equipment for aviation communications and tactical Army frequency modulation equipment for communications with tactical forces. In addition to its airborne activities, the Army provides personnel and operations for four air traffic control areas. The Corps of Engineers (Civil Works) maintains 41,000 kilometers of navigable waterways, locks, and local traffic controls. In this role, nationally established maritime radio facilities and procedures are used. In addition, the Corps of Engineers operates a fleet to support its missions, which operate on Army channels.

In addition to its maritime activities, the Corps of Engineers operates radio sensing and remote controls for 66,000 dams with most of them producing electric power. This requires approximately 1,600 kilometers of microwave radio relay systems. The total number of radio frequencies used by the Corps of Engineers may be illustrated by the fact that one third of all Army frequency assignment actions in the conterminous United States are for Corps activities.

Department of the Navy

The Department of the Navy includes the Executive Office of the Secretary of the Navy, the Office of the Chief of Naval Operations, the Headquarters U.S. Marine Corps, and other commands and activities located in Washington, D.C.; the entire operating forces of the Navy and Marine Corps, including reserve components; all shore and field activities under the control of the Secretary of the Navy; and, in time of war or when the President so directs, the U.S. Coast Guard (USCG). Navy and Marine Corps forces are organized, equipped, trained, and prepared to maintain a constant state of readiness for immediate and sustained offensive and defensive operations on and under the seas, on land, and in the air.

Since the end of the Cold War, the Navy has been redefining missions and concepts of operations, in recognition of the new military challenges presented by the post-Cold War world. The over-arching document, *"Forward...From the Sea",* offers a new vision based on revised strategy and military operational needs for regional conflicts in the world's littoral zones and on new technological capabilities for current and future use. The future warfighting environment will involve cooperative, long-range engagements and require a highly responsive command, control, communications, computers, intelligence, surveillance and reconnaissance (C4ISR) decision cycle. This projected future environment has moved information and the requirement for information superiority to center stage in all thinking about the conduct of naval warfare. Warfighters now require information superiority – the capability to collect, process and disseminate information, while denying an adversary's ability to do the same. The requirement for information superiority was a key element in the development of the naval vision for C4ISR, known as Copernicus. Copernicus is the initiative to gain information superiority and make C4ISR systems responsive to the warfighter; to field these systems quickly; to capitalize on advances in technology; and to shape doctrine to reflect these changes. Embodied in the Copernicus initiative is the naval concept of

Network Centric Warfare (NCW) which is the vision for complete integration of C4ISR systems.

The Navy's overarching program for achieving the command and control elements of NCW is Information Technology for the 21st Century (IT21). As first steps toward implementing IT21 requirements and meeting NCW, the Navy has begun fielding several command, control, communications, computers, and intelligence (C4I) programs. While there are a number of programs under development, the following represent the thrust of IT21: The Global Command and Control System - Maritime program provides for the common operational picture and collaborative planning in the near term, Link 16 provides a portion of the Coherent Tactical Picture, and the Cooperative Engagement Capability (CEC) for air and missile defense. CEC manifests the potential to increase combat effectiveness by linking geographically dispersed sensors, of differing capabilities, with all potential firing platforms.

Operational Maneuver from the Sea (OMFTS) is the Marine Corps' capstone operational concept "for maritime power projection." OMFTS was precipitated by two fundamental changes in the operational environment: (1) the prominence of the threat characterized by the phrase "chaos in the littorals" and, (2) enhanced tactical capabilities based on technical advances in information management, battlefield mobility, and lethality of conventional weapons. The concept presents a vision of what "operational maneuver from the sea" is and what capabilities naval forces of the near future should possess. Given the significantly greater distance from which movement ashore will begin, compared to current operations, and that there will be no intermediate pause on the way to the objective, OMFTS requires vastly greater C4ISR capabilities than those of today.

Operation of C-E equipment, systems, and subsystems is a necessity to support, coordinate, and control Marine Air/Ground Task Forces and other independently operating Fleet Marine Force units. The equipments and systems that require frequency spectrum are tactical radios, sensors, battlefield surveillance radars, air defense radars, tactical data link terminals, and satellite communications links. To meet the response requirements associated with the U.S. Marine Corps mission, amphibious training exercises are conducted routinely on a worldwide basis, often in conjunction with allied forces.

To achieve the coordination necessary to conduct joint operations, naval forces require the capability to 'train as you fight' within the United States and its Possessions (USP) and littoral waters. The radio frequency spectrum is the only medium that can support the Navy and Marine Corps' increased mobile communications requirements associated with NCW and OMFTS. Assured access to the electromagnetic spectrum is essential for the Department of the Navy strategic and tactical systems to fulfill their communications, intelligence, surveillance, reconnaissance, and weapons guidance missions both in times of peace and during conflict.

The operating forces of the Navy and Marine Corps are a primary means of force projection and peacekeeping in furtherance of national policy. Operations can be conducted unilaterally, jointly with forces of other U.S. military services, and with allied forces in combined operations. Such operations bring a heavy concentration of sophisticated electronics systems into a constrained area and place heavy demands on the electromagnetic spectrum to accommodate the necessary C4ISR flow without mutual electromagnetic interference. The sophisticated defensive and offensive detection, location, and weapon systems necessary to accomplish the mission also place heavy demands on management and use of the electromagnetic spectrum.

Office of the Chief of Naval Operations (OPNAV) and the Director, SpaceInformation Warfare, Command and Control Directorate (CNO N6)

The Chief of Naval Operations (CNO) is the senior military officer in the Navy. A member of the Joint Chiefs of Staff, the CNO is the principal naval advisor to the President and to the Secretary of the Navy on the conduct of war, and is the principal advisor and naval executive to the Secretary on the conduct of naval activities of the Department of the Navy. Assistants are the Vice Chief of Naval Operations, the Deputy Chiefs of Naval Operations and a number of other ranking officers. These officers and their staffs are collectively known as the CNO N6 (OpNav).

The Director, Space Information Warfare, Command and Control, Office of the Chief of Naval Operations (CNO N6) provides Navy space and electronic warfare leadership, vision, policy resources and doctrine support of naval, joint and combined operating forces. CNO N6 has the responsibility to develop Navy communications systems and information networks, including strategic and space communications, and to act as the resource and program sponsor for those programs. The Director also exercises policy direction and control, administration and management of the Naval Telecommunications System (NTS). The paramount mission of OPNAV N6 is to ensure that the fleet is properly equipped with and trained to use the best possible Command, Control and Intelligence (C2I), space, information warfare and information technology communication networks that are affordable and that meet the warfighters requirements; and that the NTS is responsive to operational commanders, including Joint Commanders.

Headquarters, United States Marine Corps, Command, Control, Communications, Computers and Intelligence (C4I)

The Assistant Chief of Staff, Command, Control, Communications, and Computers (AC/S C4) is responsible for planning, directing, coordinating, and oversight of all Headquarters, Marine Corps matters which relate to C4. As the senior C4 proponent, the AC/S C4 is the center of C4 policy, oversight of standards, and systems integration within the Marine Corps. He provides C4 leadership, education and vision to the Marine Corps. The AC/S C4 monitors internal C4 systems as well as all DOD, national, and allied systems that impact on the Marine Corps C4 Architecture for both the Fleet Marine Force and the Supporting Establishment to ensure systems integration and interoperability.

Naval Electromagnetic Spectrum Center (NAVEMSCEN)

NAVEMSCEN manages the Department of the Navy's (DON) use of the radio frequency electromagnetic spectrum needed for the control and exploitation of sea, air, and space. NAVEMSCEN is the Navy's primary responsible organization for implementation of the CNO electromagnetic spectrum management policy and procedures. The NAVEMSCEN provides direct support to operational radio frequency spectrum users by obtaining and documenting all frequency assignments used to support Navy and Marine Corps operations worldwide. They also register Navy and Marine Corps HF and satellite frequency assignments with the Radiocommunications Bureau of the ITU. NAVEMSCEN's primary responsibilities are:

- Represent its Service C4I Chief (CNO N6) on spectrum management issues

- Coordinate spectrum management issues within joint, DOD, national, and international forums

- Partner with the acquisition and operational communities of the DON to actively assist them in identifying and following the spectrum management process.

Major Systems Commands (SYSCOMS)

Naval Sea Systems Command (NAVSEASYSCOM)

The NAVSEASYSCOM is the Navy Department's central activity for designing, engineering, integrating, building and procuring U.S. Naval ships and shipboard weapons and combat systems. NAVSEASYSCOM's responsibilities also include the maintenance, repair, modernization and conversion of in-service ships and their weapons and combat systems. Additionally, it provides technical, industrial, and logistics support for naval ships, and ensures the proper design and development of the total ship, including contractor-furnished shipboard systems.

Other important NAVSEASYSCOM functions include introduction of ships to the Fleet; the Navy's salvage and diving operation; explosive ordnance safety and disposal; coordination of naval ship conversion and repair for both the DOD and the Military Sealift Command; and support of ship construction for the Maritime Administration. NAVSEASYSCOM manages 135 acquisition programs, which are assigned to the Command's 7 affiliated Program Executive Offices (PEOs) and various Headquarters elements. Organizationally, as of 1 June 1998, the Command had 38 subordinate shore activities and more than 150 detachments and on-site offices. These organizations are located all over the United States and a small number are overseas.

Naval Air Systems Command (NAVAIRSYSCOM)

The Naval Aviation Systems Team (TEAM) comprises:

- Program Executive Office, Air Anti-Submarine Warfare, Assault, and Special Mission Programs PEO(A)
- Program Executive Office, Strike Weapons and Unmanned Aviation PEO(W)
- Program Executive Office, Tactical Aircraft Programs PEO(T) and
- Program Executive Office, Joint Strike Fighter PEO(JSF)

Working with industry, the TEAM delivers high quality, affordable products and support to the operating forces. Products and services delivered on behalf of the customer include: aircraft, avionics, air-launched weapons, electronic warfare systems, cruise missiles, unmanned aerial vehicles, launch and arresting gear, training equipment and facilities, and all other equipment related to Navy and Marine Corps air power. Total life cycle support of all naval aviation weapons systems include: research, design, development, and engineering; acquisition; test and evaluation; training facilities and equipment; repair and modification; and in-service engineering and logistics support.

Ultimately, NAVAIRSYSCOM's goal parallels that of their customers - to reconstitute the Fleet's assets with new and modernized weapons systems, technically and functionally capable of responding to the demands of the 21st century.

Space and Naval Warfare Systems Command (SPAWARSYSCOM)

SPAWARSYSCOM is responsible for directing the development, acquisition, and life cycle management of C4ISR systems for the U.S. Navy, and select Marine Corps and joint service programs. The majority of the frequencies within the DON are generated by the use of

C4ISR systems under SPAWAR cognizance. The mission of SPAWAR is to provide Naval commanders a decisive warfare advantage through the development, acquisition, and life cycle management of effective and responsive:

- Undersea, terrestrial, and space sensors
- Battle management systems
- Information transfer systems
- Information management systems, and
- Systems for selective denial of these capabilities to opposing forces.

To implement this mission, SPAWAR is organized into six Program Directorates (PD) with a Chief Engineers Office that supports the entire command:

- Advanced Concepts and Technology PD
- Space Technology Systems PD
- Global Information and Network Systems PD
- Information Warfare Systems PD
- Communications System PD
- ISR Systems PD
- Office of Chief Engineer

In addition, there are three systems centers that provide engineering and technical support to the program directorates:

- SPAWAR Systems Center, Charleston
- SPAWAR Systems Center, Chesapeake
- SPAWAR Systems center, San Diego

Department of the Air Force

The mission of the U.S. Air Force (USAF) is to defend the United States through the control and exploitation of air and space. To accomplish this mission, the Air Force uses several subsidiary organizations, the first level of which includes the Major Commands (MAJCOMs). The MAJCOMs are assigned specific duties and organized functionally within the conterminous United States and by geographic area overseas (to include Hawaii and Alaska). The Air Force also uses, at the same level as MAJCOMs, but separate from them and generally smaller in scope and size, Field Operating Agencies (FOAs) and Direct Reporting Units (DRUs). While MAJCOMs accomplish a broad, overall mission, FOAs and DRUs have a more specific mission. Nine MAJCOMs, two of which are outside the CONUS, exist. The following paragraphs discuss the ways in which the Air Force uses the radio frequency spectrum: first for the MAJCOMs; then one FOA: the Air Intelligence Agency; then two subordinate units: the Air Force Frequency Management Agency and the Air Force Communications Agency both of which are DRUs of the HQ Air Force Communications and Information Center; then one organization: the Air National Guard.

Major Commands

Air Combat Command (ACC)

The ACC operates combat-coded fighters, bombers, tankers and reconnaissance aircraft, and organizes trains, equips and maintains rapid-response, combat-ready forces. ACC is the Air Force component command for the U.S. Joint Forces Command (USJFC) and U.S. Strategic Command (USSTRATCOM), and provides nuclearcapable forces for the latter. ACC subordinate numbered air forces are the air component commands for U.S. Central Command (USCENTCOM) and U.S. Southern Command (USSOUTHCOM). ACC operates specific air mobility assets in support of U.S. Transportation Command. ACC also tests new combat equipment, monitors and intercepts illegal drug traffic, and provides air defense forces for North American Aerospace Defense Command. Additionally, ACC is the lead command for the Combat Air Forces (CAF), which is made up of ACC, Pacific Air Force (PACAF), U.S. Air Forces in Europe (USAFE), Air Force Space Command (AFSPC), Air Force Special Operations Command

(AFSOC), Air Education and Training Command (AETC), Air National Guard (ANG), and Air Force Reserve (AFR).

ACC is the Air Force's largest user of the spectrum. It employs the entire range of electronic radio frequency radiating equipment including special weapon systems, navigation aids, radio location devices, and command and control systems. ACC provides aircraft and Theater Air Control System equipment to carry out close air support, air surveillance, air control, and communications connectivity within a combat zone. It also operates an extensive early warning system providing detection, identification, surveillance, and interception for national air defense. ACC is also responsible for the Air Force search and rescue and for unmanned aerial vehicle operations.

Data and communication systems used by ACC include: satellites, ground and airborne radar, Joint Surveillance System, Joint Tactical Information Distribution System, drone control and target scoring, tactical VHF and UHF air-to-ground and air-to-air systems, HF single sideband, electronic warfare and countermeasures, enemy threat simulators, navigational aids, air traffic control, and many land mobile radio systems. ACC also operates aircraft for the Airborne Battlefield Command Control Center, Airborne Warning and Control System, the Joint Surveillance Target Attack Radar System, and the National Airborne Operations Center.

ACC's worldwide mission requires extensive and continuous use of the radio frequency spectrum. The combination of ACC's unique mission requirements and complex operational systems places a heavy demand on the spectrum. As the force provider to the warfighters and the service proponent for fighter and bomber operations, ACC's mission of putting bombs on target could not be met without unencumbered use of the spectrum.

Air Education and Training Command

Known as the "First Command", AETC recruits, accesses, commissions, trains, and educates Air Force enlisted and officer personnel. AETC provides basic military training; basic and advanced technical training; flying training; and professional military and degree-granting professional continuing education for officer, enlisted, and civilian personnel. AETC conducts joint, medical service, and readiness training and Air Force security assistance training for allied and friendly foreign nations. AETC's charter is fostering an Expeditionary Air Force (EAF) culture in our recruits and officers. It also prepares mission-ready graduates, people who are ready to perform their mission and provide combat support to worldwide operations. AETC continues to contributes a major role in the development and evolution of our aerospace forces.

AETC spectrum usage is as diverse as the rest of the Air Force with the "train as you fight" concept. Communications systems used in operational support and training bases include VHF/UHF air-to-ground and air-to-air systems, navigational aids, air traffic control, land mobile radio, radar, microwave, HF, threat simulators, drone control, and target scoring and satellite communications.

Air Force Materiel Command (AFMC)

Through integrated management of research, development, test, acquisition, and support, AFMC advances and uses technology to acquire and sustain superior systems in partnership with its customers. AFMC performs continuous product and process improvement throughout the life cycle. As an integrated part of the Air Force warfighting team, AFMC contributes to affordable combat superiority, readiness, and sustainability.

AFMC actively develops and acquires the most advanced systems for Air Force use, and its use of the radio frequency spectrum is as wide as that of the entire Air Force. Approximately one-fifth of the radio frequency assignments for Air Force operations are to satisfy AFMC requirements. Recognition of the radio frequency spectrum as a finite and vital resource requiring prudent use and management is intrinsic to the AFMC mission. The enhancement of national defense would be diminished if new USAF equipment were not compatible with intended environments or were in frequency bands either overcrowded or allocated for different radio services. Research, development, test, and support activities conducted at AFMC laboratories, product centers, air logistics centers, base operating sites, test ranges, and those at the facilities of contractors rely heavily on the radio frequency spectrum.

Air Force Space Command

The AFSPC operates space and ballistic missile systems, including ballistic missile warning, space control, spacelift, and satellite operations. AFSPC supports terrestrial forces, and civil and commercial space activities. AFSPC supplies: Air Force Satellite Control Network, Ballistic Missile Warning System, Cobra Dane radar, Defense Meteorological Satellite Program, Defense Satellite Communications System, and other military satellite communications systems such as Military Strategic and Tactical Relay, Defense Support Program satellites, the Fleet Satellite Communications System, the Global Positioning System (GPS), Ground-based Electro-Optical Deep Space Surveillance System, North Atlantic Treaty Organization (NATO) III communications satellites, Passive Space Surveillance System, Pave Paws radars, and Perimeter Attack Characterization System.

AFSPC, which is responsible for all Air Force and many DOD, U.S., and NATO satellite systems, has an extensive need for radio frequency spectrum. Each satellite needs telemetry, command, and control, and many are used specifically for radio frequency communications. Since most satellite receivers are extremely sensitive, they must be protected from spurious emissions from other transmitters. The warfighter needs satellite communications during the entire conflict. Moreover, the DOD and our allies need the radio frequency spectrum for the safety and well-being of the warfighters in a hostile, foreign land.

Air Force Special Operations Command

The AFSOC is the Air Force component of U.S. Special Operations Command. AFSOC deploys specialized air power, delivering special operations combat power anywhere, anytime. AFSOC provides unconventional warfare, direct action, special reconnaissance, counter terrorism, and foreign internal defense support to the Unified Commands. AFSOC also provides humanitarian assistance and personnel recovery, and conducts psychological and counter-narcotics operations. AFSOC assets include fixed and vertical-lift transport, aerial tankers, fixed-wing gunships, and psychological operations support aircraft. In addition to the aircrews, AFSOC personnel include Special Tactics Teams (who provide combat control and pararescue functions); Special Operations Weather Teams; and Special Operations Communications Flights. To complete its various missions worldwide, AFSOC must have extremely versatile radio-communication equipment to be compatible with that used by the forces with which it must cooperate. This includes other DOD Military Departments and foreign allies. AFSOC also needs communication and other radio frequency equipment that are interception- and jam-resistant.

Air Mobility Command (AMC)

The AMC provides rapid global airlift and aerial refueling for U.S. armed forces. AMC is the USAF component of U.S. Transportation Command, and supports wartime tasking by providing forces to theater commands. AMC also provides operational support aircraft, aeromedical evacuation missions, and visual documentation support.

There are three categories of AMC spectrum usage: fixed, tactical, and contingency or deployable. The fixed category consists of HF Automated Link Establishment for the AMC Command and Control (C2) and HF training networks. Combat Control Teams use the VHF band for tactical and joint operations for communications at drop zones/landing zones and training by the Air Mobility Warfare Center. AMC uses the VHF-AM frequency band for air traffic control operations. AMC also uses the VHF band for air-to-ground, ground-to-air, and land mobile communications for contingency and deployable operations in support of tanker Airlift Control Elements. AMC manages the super high frequency (SHF) usage for all formation aircraft using station keeping equipment within the USP and several globally assigned SHF and UHF frequencies in support of the Tanker Airlift Control Center air-to-air refueling missions. Additionally, AMC uses this band to support daily flight and command post operations. The Air Mobility Operations Groups use UHF satellite communications extensively for fixed and contingency operations. AMC uses operating frequencies in the UHF band for land mobile operations at AMC bases and for communications during deployments.

Air Force Reserve Command (AFRC)

The AFRC became a MAJCOM in accordance with the 1997 Defense Authorization Act. The Chief of Air Force Reserve also serves as commander of AFRC. HQ AFRC carries out the Chief of Staff's responsibility for command of Air Force Reserve forces. HQ AFRC participates in formulating plans for management, administration, and execution of programs affecting AFR units. The ARF provides trained units and qualified people for active duty in time of war or national emergency, or when required to maintain national security. It also performs peacetime missions compatible with training and mobilization readiness requirements. The AFR stands to meet any challenge to national defense by augmenting the active force in time of emergency.

Pacific Air Forces

The PACAF primary mission is to provide ready air and space power to promote U.S. interests in the Asia-Pacific region during peacetime, through crisis, and in war. PACAF plans, conducts and coordinates offensive and defensive air operations. PACAF organizes, trains, equips, and maintains resources to conduct air operations. PACAF's area of responsibility extends from the West Coast of the United States to the East Coast of Africa and from the Arctic to the Antarctic, more than 259 million square kilometers containing 44 countries. It operates in a multinational environment where it can interact with many different types of equipment and radio frequency standards. Alaskan and Hawaiian-based aircraft, as well as that of CONUS-based units deployed to the Pacific Theater, must interact with the equipment used in the Pacific and Asia.

Some data and communications systems used by PACAF include: satellite ground stations, ground and airborne radars, Joint Tactical Information Distribution System, tactical VHF and UHF air-to-ground and air-to air systems, HF single sideband, electronic warfare and countermeasures, enemy threat simulators, navigational aids, air traffic control, and many land mobile radio systems.

U.S. Air Forces in Europe

The USAFE trains and equips units pledged to the NATO. USAFE plans, conducts, controls, coordinates, and supports air and space operations in Europe. It supports U.S. and NATO strategies in the European/Mediterranean area and is responsible for supporting U.S. military plans and operations in parts of Europe, the Mediterranean, the Middle East, and Africa as a component of U.S. European Command. In this role, USAFE maintains fixed and mobile operating systems which use a wide variety of radio frequencies. Additionally, numerous stateside-based units augment USAFE during contingency and humanitarian operations and exercises, and when Presidential and VIP missions includes, but is not limited to HF point-to-point, VHF air-to-ground and point-to-point, UHF air-to-ground and tactical satellite, all air traffic control services frequency bands, portions of the 1700–1850 MHz and 2300–2400 MHz ranges for air-to-air combat training, 5000–6000 MHz for the control of unmanned aerial vehicles and tactical weather radars, and, due to the high satellite links in the 12–14 GHz range. Since USAFE also has to interact with many different countries, its equipment must be compatible with many different types of equipment and radio frequency standards, including the United States.

Field Operating Agencies

Air Intelligence Agency (AIA)

The AIA provides direct intelligence security, electronic combat, foreign technology, and treaty monitoring support to national leaders and field air component commanders. The AIA provides combat commanders data that enables them to decide when to exploit, jam, deceive, or destroy hostile military communications. The AIA delivers human intelligence and scientific and technical intelligence. It provides measurement and signature intelligence data collection, analysis and exploitation support, and nuclear intelligence production support. In the age of information warfare, the AIA is extremely important since it not only helps gather information from possible and real enemies, but also keeps them from doing the same to the United States and its allies.

To be successful, AIA must have real-time data gathering from its units around the globe, and real-time data distribution to commanders in the field. To do this, AIA needs a large amount of radio frequency spectrum, as there is no other way to ensure global connectivity in a variable, unstable environment, such as an armed conflict or war. The AIA uses satellite communications for real-time global connectivity with all of its locations. Because of the sensitivity and essentiality of its communications, it is critical that these communications are not intercepted or corrupted. The AIA uses UHF air-to-ground communications with its airborne units, and has a worldwide UHF satellite intelligence network for data gathering and distribution. The AIA, in conjunction with the Department of Energy (DOE), also uses UHF satellite communications for verification of conformance with the Nuclear Proliferation and Consolidated Test Band Treaties.

Subordinate Units under Direct Report Units

Air Force Communications Agency (AFCA)

The AFCA ensures command, control, communications, and computer (C4) systems across the Air Force are integrated and interoperable. They develop and validate C4 architectures, technical standards, requirements, policies, procedures, and technical solutions.

The AFCA does not itself have a large need for the radio frequency spectrum. Nevertheless, in conjunction with the Joint Technical Architecture-Air Force, it helps to ensure the Air Force's equipment uses the spectrum efficiently and productively and that the equipment is interoperable with the other equipment used in the Air Force and the DOD. The AFCA ensures that all Air Force C4 acquisitions are compatible and interoperable with other existing or proposed C4 systems. They extensively test new civil technologies being acquired for Air Force use to ensure compatibility.

Air Force Frequency Management Agency (AFFMA)

The AFFMA serves as the Air Force executive agent for implementing Air Force use of the radio frequency spectrum. It provides the Air Force with global electromagnetic spectrum access anytime, anywhere. AFFMA develops and implements Air Force radio frequency spectrum management guidelines and instructions to support the Air Force mission. The AFFMA is directly responsible to the Commander, Air Force Communications and Information Center for all Air Force radio frequency spectrum management matters.

The AFFMA provides support to operational radio frequency spectrum users by obtaining and documenting frequency assignments used to support Air Force operations worldwide. They register Air Force HF and satellite frequency assignments with the Radio-communications Bureau of the ITU. They represent, advocate, and defend Air Force interests in spectrum management matters on various DOD, national, and international committees, groups, and organizations to include the Technical Subcommittee, Frequency Assignment Subcommittee, and the Spectrum Planning Subcommittee of the IRAC as well as being the Air Force executive agent for the Air Force Electromagnetic Environmental Effects Program. They also coordinate assignment actions with Unified Commands for operations outside the USP. The AFFMA does not itself use the radio frequency spectrum.

Air Force Organization

Air National Guard

The mission of the ANG is to enforce Federal authority, suppress insurrection and defend the Nation when mobilized by the President, Congress, or both. Commanded by the governors of the 50 States, Puerto Rico, Guam, the Virgin Islands, and the commanding general of the District of Columbia. Each governor is represented in the state or territory chain of command by an adjutant general.

The ANG has operational components of ACC, AETC, AFSOC, AMC and PACAF, and therefore has a need to have component equipment from all of these NWCOMS. Equipment used by these MAJCOMs might also be used by the ANG, so its radio frequency spectrum use is very wide. The ANG also operates during a time of national emergency or natural disaster, as well as during war or armed conflict, so they have a continuous need for the radio frequency spectrum.

National Test Ranges

The national test ranges test missiles and other major weapons systems that are critical to the Nation's defense. All of the U.S. military services (Army, Navy, Air Force, and Marine Corps), conduct test programs for major weapons systems, and use of the radio frequency spectrum is critical to the operation of these test programs. The demand for radio frequency spectrum during land, sea, and air force weapons systems testing and training, in particular during joint exercises, is greater today than ever before.

At the lower end of the spectrum, ground-to-air, air-to-air, and ground-to-ground VHF/UHF for aircraft communications and land mobile radio systems are continually used to provide positive control of test range operations. Flight termination frequencies provide for safety concerns. Data links cover a wide range of operations including fixed microwave links, weapon and missile data links, telemetry for real-time data and video, and instrumentation control links starting and controlling tracking cameras, and various other event critical activities. Testing sophisticated vehicles (aircraft, land vehicles, sea craft, rockets, and missiles) require enormous amounts of performance data. Further uses of data links include remotely controlled explosive ordinance disposal systems, control of sub-scale and full-scale drone aircraft and other unmanned aerial vehicles, and command control and command destruct links.

Radar systems are vital for many aspects of testing. Uses include: missile and aircraft tracking radars with associated transponders, air traffic control radars, weapon scoring systems, weather radars for monitoring weather conditions that might affect a test mission, and missile guidance radars. Aircraft and missile testing require extensive communications linking tracking and data collection sites over large areas.

Finally, the development and testing of electronic countermeasures (ECM), electronic counter-countermeasures (ECCM), or Electronic Attack (EA) systems are major activities at many national test/training ranges. Many ranges are used for routine ECM/ECCM/EA training of combat aircrews. ECM/ECCM/EA systems are used to jam, confuse or otherwise render potential enemy radio frequency weapons systems (such as radar guided missiles, surveillance radars, and jammers) ineffective. ECM testing against simulated threat system radars is critical to development and testing of our advanced technology weapon systems electromagnetic countermeasures to find their capabilities, vulnerabilities, and weaknesses.

Reserve Components

In addition to the regular Armed Forces, there are reserve units of the Army, Navy, Air Force, and Marine Corps, including the Army National Guard, Air National Guard, and the Coast Guard in the United States. The mission of the reserve is to provide trained units and qualified personnel to augment the active duty forces and to provide a combat-ready team during time of war, national emergency or when required to maintain national security. Reserve units perform peacetime missions that are compatible with training and mobilization readiness requirements. The reserve routinely conducts exercises with extensive use of C-E equipments and relies heavily on all parts of the radio frequency spectrum for its communications, command, and control capabilities. Since the reserve units must be combat ready at any time, they must train with the same equipment as active-duty personnel, and they have the same radio frequency spectrum requirements as their active duty counterparts throughout U.S. forces worldwide.

Department of Agriculture

The majority of radio use within the Department of Agriculture (USDA) resides with the Forest Service (FS) supporting the protection and management of National Forests, National Grasslands, and Wilderness Areas, which comprise approximately 192 million acres. Forest Service radio systems, comprised of over 60,000 radios, are used in programs supporting incident communications such as wildfire firefighting, law enforcement, and emergency disaster control (earthquakes, volcanic eruptions, hurricanes, etc.). Wildland firefighting activities are supported with over 40 FS owned fixed-wing aircraft, over 40 contracted fixed-wing aircraft, and almost 500 contract helicopters. Law enforcement activities in drug control alone include over 300,000 petty offense violations and over 2,000 arrests annually. Other uses of these systems include the administrative and operational uses supporting timber production, recreation sites (almost 6,000 campgrounds), watershed and water supply, wildlife and grassland conservation, and forest research.

Some additional 6,500 additional pieces of radio equipment are devoted to the support of other agricultural, hydrologic, and research activities. The increasing communications needs of the Natural Resources Conservation Service (NRCS), the Animal and Plant Health Inspection Service (APHIS), and other USDA agencies have resulted in a rapid increase in the numbers of radios. Examples are the NRCS Meteor Burst Hydrologic system in the West and APHIS's border, airport, and port inspection, animal disease control, and plant protection and quarantine activities.

Department of Commerce

In the Department of Commerce, the largest user of the radio spectrum is the *National Oceanic and Atmospheric Administration (NOAA),* which manages, conserves and monitors marine resources, and predicts atmospheric and marine conditions for the protection of life and property. The *National Weather Service (NWS),* with personnel located at 121 Weather Forecast Offices throughout the United States, is charged with observing and reporting the weather, issuing forecasts and warning of weather and flood conditions affecting national safety, welfare, and economy. Its seven National Centers for Environmental Prediction are key centers in long range and regional forecasting for the World Meteorological Organization of the United Nations. Its Tropical Prediction Center also tracks hurricanes and forecasts their movement and intensity to provide early warnings to populated areas in the storm path.

NWS operates about 120 weather radars, 102 weather balloon stations, 503 NOAA Weather Radio Stations, and, together with state and local governments, 3,437 hydrological data collection and warning stations. It also operates many other radio stations serving the Geostationary Operational Environmental Satellite (GOES, platform station) Program, the hydrologic telemetry program, the fire-weather program, the hurricane backup communications program, the weather reconnaissance aircraft program, and other miscellaneous radio requirements.

The *National Environmental Satellite, Data, and Information Service (NESDIS)* operates remote sensing satellites which make day and night observations of weather (clouds, temperature, and winds), ocean state (sea surface temperature), geological and agricultural features over the entire Earth. These data and other environmental data are transmitted to ground stations by satellite transmitters using radio frequencies. The data are gathered at the ground and retransmitted via commercial satellites to a central processing center. The meteorological satellite system also provides for the collection and radio relay of data from fixed and mobile environmental observing platforms (ships, aircraft, ocean buoys, and remote surface sites).

The NOAA Data Buoy Center develops and operates environmental data buoys for weather monitoring, prediction, and various other scientific programs. Data is sent from the buoys and platforms via UHF signals through the GOES and NOAA satellites to land via down-links near 1700 MHz. There are over 10,000 data collection platforms currently using the data collection radio relay service of the meteorological satellites. These observation platforms are operated by NOAA, other government agencies, and private industry to obtain data on stream flow and water quality, snow depth, and rainfall in remote mountain areas, oceanic measurements from buoys and remote islands, and wind and temperature information from commercial aircraft.

The polar orbiting weather satellites of the NOAA include Search And Rescue Satellite (SARSAT) System packages that detect distress signals sent by radio to the satellite and provides location information with a 2–5 kilometers resolution. There are presently three ground stations in the United States, one in Canada, one in France, and three in Russia that receive the transmitted data from the SARSAT. In addition, NESDIS operates the National Geophysical Data Center collecting data from 33 worldwide ionospheric sounders (low frequency through HF bands).

The *National Marine Fisheries Service (NMFS)* conducts exploratory fishing as well as fish and marine mammal population research programs utilizing HF and VHF radio equipment to provide tracking and migration information as well as communications between major fishery centers and research ships of the NOAA Corps Fleet. NMFS also enforces Federal fish and wildlife conservation laws relating to the living marine resources within the United States 320-kilometer jurisdictional fishery conservation zone. VHF radio communications is an essential factor during these operations.

The *National Ocean Service (NOS)* radio-communication facilities are used to support some 23 ships and 18 mobile field parties engaged in oceanographic, marine and geodetic surveys, and NMFS activities. These programs, activities, and related radio-communications are conducted by the NOS to measure the Earth's surface, its coastlines and its undersea structure, and to provide information on the marine environment and its resources for use by scientists and the public. NOS also publishes numerous nautical charts for use by mariners for improved safety of life at sea. Communications are principally for safety, control of navigation, operations, medical emergencies, and administrative messages between ships conducting joint operations and between ships and shore stations using NOS, NMFS, Navy, and USCG commercial communication circuits. The Charting and Geodetic Services, an office of NOS, also utilize radio frequencies in the visible and infrared spectrums for very precise distance measurements. The VHF frequency band is used for voice communications between field parties, including the Office of Oceanography and Marine Assessment who uses radio-communications to coordinate clean-up teams and track movement of contamination when responding to oil and hazardous chemical spills.

The *National Institute of Standards and Technology (NIST),* through its Boulder, Colorado facilities, is responsible for primary time and frequency standards, and dissemination of these data through radio stations WWV and WWVB in Colorado and WWVH in Hawaii to over 100,000 listeners throughout the world. Data is also disseminated through dial-up telephone service (2 million users per year) as well as GOES and GPS satellites. High precision time signals are sent and received from domestic communication satellites at 14 and 12 GHz. NIST also conducts extensive experimentation using the radio spectrum in such areas as testing instruments for earthquake calibration measurements. Specific areas of radio usage include communication, data telemetry, and satellite transfer of information.

The Department of Energy

Mission

The DOE was established under Public Law 95–91 of 1977, by consolidating energy functions within the Federal Government. Its mission is to provide information and the scientific and educational foundation for the technology, policy, and institutional leadership necessary to achieve efficiency in energy use, diversity in energy sources, a more productive and competitive economy, improved environmental quality, and a secure national defense. In support of this mission, DOE has identified five business lines that most effectively use and integrate its unique scientific and technological assets, engineering expertise, and facilities for the benefit of the Nation. These five business lines are: economic productivity, energy resources, science and technology, national security, and environmental quality.

An Overview of Current Spectrum Use

Although each of DOE's five business lines uses spectrum resources, the energy resources and national security business lines use the most. Land mobile systems primarily support the other business lines — economic productivity, science and technology, and environmental quality. Both conventional and trunked land mobile systems are deployed. The spectrum use for each DOE business line is discussed in the following paragraphs.

National Security

This business line supports and maintains a safe, secure, reliable, and smaller nuclear weapons stockpile without nuclear testing; safely dismantles and disposes of excess weapons; and provides the technical leadership for national and global non-proliferation to reduce the continuing and new nuclear dangers in the world. Initiatives include the National Ignition Facility, the Advanced Strategic Computing Program, the Non-proliferation and Verification Research and Development Programs, and the Los Alamos Neutron Science Center. DOE places primary importance on safely dismantling nuclear warheads, ensuring the safety of operations, protecting the environment, managing our nuclear weapons complex, and cost-effectively consolidating our non-nuclear manufacturing activities.

Science and Technology

The objective of this business line is to use the unique resources of the Department's $30 billion laboratories and their 40,000 scientists and engineers to maintain world-class leadership in basic and applied research in support of the Department's other business lines. Fundamental research maintains the Nation's world leadership in science, mathematics, and engineering. Research in energy and environmental sciences is paving the way for a more sustainable energy future. Opening our scientific and technological resources to industry will improve the Nation's productivity and economic growth.

Energy Resources

This business line develops and deploys energy efficient and renewable energy technologies; advances the efficient and environmentally responsible production, transportation, and use of conventional energy sources; promotes the development of sustainable energy technologies with high export potential; promotes an equitable system of energy supply and end use; and reduces U.S. vulnerability to energy supply disruptions. In carrying out the Energy Policy Act of 1992, DOE's programs are expected to save homeowners $17 billion and businesses $12.5 billion per year by 2005 and to create almost 310,000 jobs. Moreover, DOE's transportation technology programs are expected to reduce oil imports by 2.3 million barrels a day by 2000, creating a savings for drivers and improve the balance of trade by $47 million per year.

Power Marketing Administrations

The five Power Marketing Administrations market electricity generated primarily by 125 Federal hydropower projects throughout 33 states from Alaska to the East Coast. The electrical energy is carried over more than 56,000 kilometers of high voltage transmission lines to serve Federal, public bodies, and cooperatives. Revenues from selling electricity are used to repay annual operation and maintenance costs, repay the capital investments with interest, and assist capital repayment on irrigation features of certain projects.

The distribution of electrical energy from the generating plants to the load centers and the interconnection of bulk electrical power supply systems for reliability and adequacy have resulted in extremely complex national networks aimed at the optimum economic configuration. The systems have, as integral and critical parts, extensive administrative and operational telecommunications for voice and data transmissions to prevent brownouts and blackouts. These facilities must be of the highest reliability, economically and technically feasible, and must be instantly available for the successful operation of the Nation's electrical power systems. Some of these telecommunications facilities are shared with other Federal departments and agencies and some must interface with utilities of the private sector.

Petroleum Reserves

The Strategic Petroleum Reserve, created in 1975, gives the United States adequate strategic and economic protection against severe oil supply disruptions. The Strategic Petroleum Reserve program provides for the storage of 680 million barrels of crude oil in underground salt caverns at five sites in the Gulf Coast area and connected to major private sector distribution systems. The Naval Petroleum and Oil Shale Reserves were established by a series of Executive Orders between 1912 and 1924 to provide emergency liquid fuel supplies for national defense. Oil production at the three sites since they have been opened has been approximately 750 million barrels. Natural gas production at these sites has been about one billion cubic feet. Natural liquid gas production at these sites has been approximately two billion gallons.

Environmental Quality

This business line protects public health and the environment by understanding and reducing the environmental, safety, and health risks and threats from DOE facilities and develops the technologies and institutions required for solving domestic and global problems.

Economic Productivity

This business line promotes sustained U.S. economic growth by stimulating the creation of high-wage jobs and diversity in research and development collaborations with industry and universities. This growth further helps drive products into the domestic and international marketplace, helps industry become more competitive by cost-effectively shifting from waste management to resource efficiency and pollution prevention, and stimulates global DOE technology usage and exports. The DOE's vast technological and research resources can thus enhance industry's productivity and maximize the return on taxpayer investment in those resources by providing economic benefits to the Nation that go beyond the original mission of the laboratories.

Summary of DOE Spectrum Use

The DOE, at an investment of almost $1 billion, has about 9,600 frequency authorizations supporting mission, programmatic, and operational requirements. These systems include HF, land mobile, aeronautical and maritime mobile, microwave, satellites, radar, navigation, telemetry, and surveillance systems. In addition, DOE uses more than 1,000 power line carrier systems to manage and control the distribution of electrical energy.

The DOE's current radio systems operate at specific frequencies between 200 kHz and 35 GHz. About 60 percent of the Department's spectrum resources are used for land mobile systems followed by 25 percent for microwave systems and 10 percent for HF systems for emergency purposes. The remaining 5 percent is for radar, telemetry, and satellite services. DOE's power line carrier systems operate at selected frequencies between 8 kHz and 496 kHz.

Federal Emergency Management Agency

The Federal Emergency Management Agency (FEMA) was established in the Executive Branch as an independent agency in 1979 to provide a single point of accountability for all Federal emergency preparedness, mitigation and response activities. FEMA develops, coordinates, and executes plans and programs providing for continuity and effective operation of the Federal Government during national emergencies; provides facilities and resources for management and coordination of emergency information; and provides centralized coordination and control and day-to-day management of the National Emergency Management System (NEMS). NEMS consists of the total telecommunications and data processing resources necessary for FEMA to accomplish its assigned peacetime and wartime functional responsibilities and meet all established operational requirements under the Integrated Emergency Management System umbrella. Current capabilities of NEMS include the National Warning System, the FEMA National Teletype System, the FEMA National Voice

System, the FEMA National Radio System, and the capability to activate the Emergency Broadcast System at the direction of the President.

General Services Administration

The General Services Administration (GSA) has the responsibility to protect Federal property under its charge and control and to ensure a safe, secure environment for conducting Government activities. Protection includes: 21,000 space assignments, housing 887,000 Federal employees in 6,800 government-owned and leased buildings. The primary use of GSA's radio systems are for law enforcement and buildings management operation. The radio frequency system includes portables and mobiles, base stations, paging, intrusion detection, access control and closed circuit television. The total GSA investment in radio frequency equipment is in excess of $40 million.

Department of Health and Human Services

The principal user of radio spectrum in the Department of Health and Human Services (DHHS) is the Public Health Service (PHS). The Indian Health Service (IHS), a PHS operating agency, is responsible for about 80 percent of the approximately 1,450 frequency assignments utilized by DHHS. The IHS supports the delivery of health care to Native Americans by using radio to communicate with emergency medical vehicles, remote health stations and mobile health units. Radio is also used extensively for paging systems to communicate with key medical personnel. In Alaska, the IHS uses both HF radio and common carrier satellite communications to provide "Doctor Call" assistance to village health aides at isolated locations. IHS radio base stations at 50 hospitals also communicate with 60 tribal government ambulance services for dispatch and control to respond to serious medical emergencies at remote Indian locations. Radio frequencies are used in remote areas in support of fresh water systems. The IHS participates in state emergency radio networks to coordinate the rendition or delivery of medical care using medical radio communications frequencies.

The Center for Devices and Radiological Health, Food and Drug Administration, the Lister Hill National Center for Biomedical Communications, and National Institute of Health (NIH) use frequencies for experimental purposes. The NIH also uses radio frequencies to support their campus operation with paging, maintenance, administration, law enforcement, fire and public safety. The PHS also uses radio frequencies for bio-medical telemetry to conduct medical research and for monitoring the treatment of patients. Radio frequencies are used by the Office of the Secretary and DHHS operation divisions for communications to control various security and administrative operations.

The DHHS Office of Emergency Preparedness uses radio frequencies to support their Disaster Medical Assistance Teams. These teams are deployed in times of natural and man-made disasters. Teams have served in areas hit by hurricanes, earthquakes, and bombs. Teams were deployed for Operation Desert Storm. Radio communication is critical for the deployment, operation, and logistical support of these teams.

Department of the Interior

The Department of the Interior is custodian of 750 million acres of land and is charged with the conservation and development of the Nation's natural resources. It has a wide variety of radio operations throughout the spectrum distributed among nine operating bureaus with diverse missions serving the public and protecting the country's natural resources. The major activities using radio are for point-to-point fixed base station and mobile radios. These are used by the Bureau of Land Management, which manages one-fifth of the Nation's gross area — some 341 million acres, for land management and protection and development of natural resources; the National Park Service, which manages some 335 parks and monuments totaling about 80 million acres, hosting more than 350 million visitors annually; the Bureau of Indian Affairs, responsible for the welfare of some 500,000 Indians and Alaskan natives on 50 million acres; the U.S. Fish and Wildlife Service, which manages over 400 National Wildlife Refuge areas, covering 90 million acres; the Geological Survey for earthquake studies, geologic and topographic mapping operations, and for the collection of hydrologic data by both terrestrial and satellite radio communication facilities; and the monitoring of off-shore oil fields by the Minerals Management Service. In all these areas of activity the primary use of radio is for the management, production and development of the Nation's natural resources, forest and range fire suppression, and protection of property and public safety.

Water management, control, and distribution by the Bureau of Reclamation is a major factor in the growth and economy of the West.

Telemetry, land mobile, and point-to-point radios are essential to the operation of the Bureau's 320 water storage dams and reservoirs, 344 diversion dams, 82,000 kilometers of carriage and distribution channels and canals, and 145 very large pumping stations. These provide irrigation for more than 12 million acres of agricultural land, providing 30 million acre feet of water for the use and consumption of over 20 million people, and water for the operation of 51 hydroelectric generating plants.

Department of Justice

The Department of Justice plays a key role in protection against criminals and subversion, in control of the country's borders, in ensuring healthy competition of business in our free enterprise system, in safeguarding the consumer, and in enforcing drug, immigration and naturalization laws. The Department also plays a significant role in protecting citizens through its efforts for effective law enforcement, crime prevention, crime detection, and the prosecution and rehabilitation of offenders.

Organized units of the Department of Justice which use or coordinate use of the radio frequency spectrum are:

- The *Federal Bureau of Investigation (FBI)* investigates all violations of Federal laws with the exception of those which have been assigned to some other Federal agency. The FBI has jurisdiction over some 185 investigative matters including espionage, sabotage and other subversive activities; kidnapping, extortion; bank robbery; and the assault or killing of the President or other Federal Officers. The FBI uses a majority of the frequency assignments listed for the Department of Justice.

- The *Immigration and Naturalization Service (INS)* administers the immigration and naturalization laws relating to the admission, exclusion, deportation, and naturalization of aliens. Through numerous enforcement activities, such as the Border Patrol, the INS protects the security of the United States' boundaries and the welfare of those legally residing in the United States.

- The *Drug Enforcement Administration (DEA)* controls narcotic and dangerous drug abuse through enforcement and demand reduction programs. The primary responsibility of DEA is to enforce U.S.

laws and statutes relating to the illegal trafficking of narcotic drugs, marijuana, depressants, stimulants, and the hallucinogenic drugs. DEA conducts domestic and international investigations of major drug traffickers concentrating efforts towards the immobilization of clandestine manufacturers, international traffickers, and the origins of diversion from legitimate channels. In addition, DEA works cooperatively with other Federal, State and local agencies as well as independently to institute national drug abuse demand reduction programs.

- The *Federal Bureau of Prisons (BOP)* supervises the operation of Federal correctional institutions and community treatment facilities; the commitment and management of Federal inmates; and the confinement and support of Federal prisoners. Correctional institutions have self-contained, dedicated communications and electronics systems to provide necessary safety and security measures.

- The *U.S. Marshals Service (USMS)* provides personal security of Federal witnesses and their families, courtroom security, protection of Federal property, and special assignments at the direction of the Attorney General. The USMS maintains the custody of Federal prisoners from time of their arrest to their commitment or release and also transports Federal prisoners pursuant to lawful writs and direction from the BOP. The USMS maintains custody and control of evidence, as well as money and property, seized pursuant to Federal statutes.

Radio systems are used by the Department of Justice to serve the national security; to safeguard life and property; and to support crime prevention and law enforcement. The radio systems used to effect these responsibilities consist primarily of land mobile radio facilities. Tactical communications among investigative, protective and enforcement personnel in the field as well as liaison communications with cooperating law enforcement organizations are essential operational tools. Mission success as well as safety of life and property is frequently dependent upon the availability of radio communications systems.

National Aeronautics and Space Administration

The National Aeronautics and Space Administration (NASA) conducts research and development in the areas of space science, astronautics, and aeronautics. With the implementation of an operational Space Transportation System — the Space Shuttle fleet — and the placing into orbit of several Tracking and Data Relay Satellites (TDRSS), NASA is forging ahead toward new horizons and the challenges that await. NASA is responsible for near and deep space exploration — using both manned and unmanned spaceflight. Also, NASA has an ongoing terrestrial and space applications program. All of NASA's research and development, and application programs are dependent on access to the radio spectrum resource.

The total NASA investment in low Earth orbit and deep space tracking facilities and other support functions – using various radio telecommunications devices and systems – is well over $2.5 billion.

From an operational point of view, NASA is currently providing launch and tracking support for approximately 45 spaceflight vehicles. This includes NASA, other Federal agency(ies), commercial, and foreign government spacecraft or satellites. Low Earth orbiting satellites are supported by the TDRSS, providing 85 percent, instead of the previous 15 percent, visibility of all on-orbit space vehicles operating below 1,200 kilometers.

National Science Foundation

The National Science Foundation (NSF) is responsible for promoting scientific knowledge, and to this end it initiates and supports fundamental and applied research in all scientific disciplines. The NSF sponsors major national and international science programs both of a special and a continuing nature throughout the Nation's academic and scientific communities, and it funds large research facilities at national centers which would be beyond the financial scope of individual institutions. Among the national centers are: the National Optical Astronomy Observatories (NOAO), the National Center for Atmospheric Research (NCAR), the National Atmosphere and Ionosphere Center (NAIC), and the National Radio Astronomy Observatory (NRAO).

NOAO operates the Cerro Tololo Inter-American Observatory in Chile, the Kitt Peak National Observatory near Tucson, Arizona, and the National Solar Observatory at Sacramento Peak, New Mexico, and is nearing completion of the two 8-meter class, new technology GEMINI telescopes, that are located in Hawaii and in Chile. NCAR operates ground and airborne radar facilities for weather research purposes. NAIC operates the Arecibo radio telescope and planetary radar, the world's largest and most sensitive single dish transit radio telescope, as well as an ionospheric heating facility.

NRAO operates the Robert C. Byrd Green Bank Telescope, Green Bank, West Virginia, that has just been completed and that is the largest moveable telescope in the world; the Very Large Array (VLA) near Socorro, New Mexico; and the Very Long Baseline Array (VLBA), which consists of 10 individual dishes distributed across the CONUS, Hawaii, and the U.S. Virgin Islands, is used to simulate a continent-wide radio telescope in terms of angular resolution. NRAO also has begun design and development of the Atacama Large Millimeter Array (ALMA), in collaboration with U.S. universities and international partners. The ALMA is going to be the world's most advanced millimeter telescope and is to be located in the High Plateau of the Andes in Chile.

The prime objective of radio spectrum management at the NSF is to ensure adequate access to the radio frequency spectrum for the scientific community's numerous research purposes. The spectrum plays a vital support role for experiments, with telemetry from remote sensing platforms such as balloons, meteorological sensors, ocean buoys, or transmitters attached to animals. Telecommunication links must be provided to coordinate experiments and to maintain contact with remote sites. While the magnitude of these activities is not comparable to active spectrum usage at other Federal agencies, the failure to adequately plan for allocations or obtain frequency assignments can adversely affect scientific objectives.

Furthermore, the NSF is responsible for protecting frequency bands for passive spectrum users—particularly radio astronomers—a responsibility which most other agencies do not share. Since frequency assignments generally are not made for passive use of the radio spectrum, they do not appear in statistical usage tables. However, radio astronomy is a major user of facilities and research funds by the NSF. Including the Robert C. Byrd Green Bank Telescope and the ALMA, U.S. investment in radio astronomy facilities will approach $1 billion. The NSF is deeply concerned with maintaining a suitable electromagnetic environment so that radio astronomy research may continue unabated.

Department of Transportation

The Department of Transportation was established to develop national transportation programs conducive to the provision of safe, fast, efficient, and convenient transportation on land, sea, and in the air. The achievement of these objectives, particularly in the air and marine environments, is totally dependent upon the continuing availability of rapid and reliable radio communications and sufficient spectrum. Radio spectrum utilization by the several operating administrations of the Department serves numerous and diverse operational and technical functions. Nevertheless, these operations have a common purpose — the enhancement of the safety factor, or one or more of the other important aspects of transportation for the general public.

The mission of the *Federal Aviation Administration (FAA)* is to provide the safest, most efficient, and responsive aviation system in the world for the benefit of the public. The FAA's success in the development and operation of the National Airspace System (NAS) plays a tremendous role in the Nation's Gross Domestic Product — the total economic activity generated by aviation is over $700 billion per year and over 8 million jobs.

To support the NAS, the FAA uses radio frequencies for communications, radio-navigation, and surveillance (radar) systems. Over 50,000 radio frequencies are assigned for use at approximately 3,000 air/ground communications sites, 1,140 instrument landing facilities, over 1,000 omnidirectional ranges, and nearly 500 radar stations.

These facilities exist to serve the flying public and to provide for their safe and efficient transportation. This includes nearly 200,000 registered private aircraft flying over 24 million hours per year; approximately 528 million passengers carried in air carrier and commuter aircraft; and nearly 23 million military flights to support our Nation's defense. FAA has an investment of approximately $10 billion of electronic equipment to support communications, navigation, and surveillance systems operating throughout the radio spectrum. In order to support the explosion in air travel in the past few years, expenditures for current and new facilities and equipment in 1996 alone will total approximately $2 billion.

In addition, FAA has annual research and development programs in excess of $500 million which are pursuing improvements in communications, navigation, and surveillance systems — nearly all of which use the radio frequency spectrum. Such programs include research and development efforts in air traffic control, navigation, precision approach and landing systems, en route and airport radars, airport surface movement, aircraft separation assurance, communications navigation and satellite initiatives, weather surveillance enhancements, and many others.

U.S. Coast Guard missions include: maritime and recreational boating safety, search and rescue services, maritime law enforcement, marine environmental protection, port safety and security, aids to navigation, marine science activities, enforcement of offshore fishery laws, suppression of smuggling and illicit drug trafficking, ice operations, both domestic and in the polar regions, maintaining a state of military readiness, and operating vessel traffic systems. The missions are carried out in behalf of the general maritime community and the use of the radio spectrum is essential in carrying out these tasks.

Radio frequencies are assigned for a variety of USCG operations including: a network of about 563 ship/shore radio stations for safety and distress communications, including maritime safety broadcasts, with the general maritime community and for command and control of its own fleet of about 255 vessels and 2,100 smaller, radio-equipped rescue craft; a network of 26 aeronautical radio stations for operational control of its fleet of about 200 aircraft; and a national network of differential GPS and long-range navigation (LORAN)-C radio navigation stations used by a variety of civil users. These operations are described in the world wide web site at: http://www.navcen.uscg.mil. The total USCG investment in C-E installations is about $1 billion. Additionally, the investment in special equipment for use with USCG operated radio navigation systems is about $600 million.

Other important uses of radio by the Department of Transportation include: a communication network of the St. Lawrence Seaway Development Corporation used to expedite and control the safe passage of U.S. and foreign vessels through the St. Lawrence Seaway; telemetering speed measurements, remote control and other technical operations carried out by the Federal Highway Administration in connection with the development of high speed rail equipment; vehicle location techniques in programs sponsored by the Urban Mass Transportation Administration; and communications supporting the rapidly developing Intelligent Transportation System.

U.S. Department of the Treasury

The U.S. Department of the Treasury enforces Federal laws pertaining to protection of the President and other designees, as well as those dealing with counterfeiting, fraud (including credit and debit card fraud), forgery, smuggling, moonshining, explosives and gun law violations, and tax evasion. Treasury agents and officers protect our borders from drug traffickers and smuggling and continually strive to protect our citizens and property from the threat of bombs, arson, and gun violence.

The majority (approximately 60 percent) of the U.S. Department of Treasury's responsibilities relates to promoting prosperous and stable American and world economies and managing the Government's finances. The law enforcement arm of the department protects our financial systems and our Nation's leaders and seeks a safe and drug-free America. Use of wireless services and devices is critical to the department's accomplishing its core missions effectively and efficiently

The Secretary of the Treasury, as the chief financial officer of the United States, advises the President on financial and tax policy matters. He has a staff of 1,600 in the office of the Secretary and oversees 120,000 employees in Washington, D.C., and 1,800 field offices throughout the United States and abroad. The Secretary of the Treasury accomplishes 98 percent of his responsibilities through Treasury's subordinate bureaus:

The *Bureau of Alcohol, Tobacco and Firearms (BATF)* is a law enforcement organization within the U.S. Department of the Treasury with responsibilities dedicated to reducing violent crimes, collecting revenue and protecting the public. The BATF enforces the Federal laws and regulations relating to alcohol, tobacco, firearms, explosives, and arson.

The *Bureau of Engraving and Printing (BEP)* produces U.S. currency, postage stamps, and other government securities that satisfy the current and future needs of the American public and the government agencies that it serves. The Bureau designs, prints, and furnishes a large variety of security products including Federal Reserve Notes, most U.S. postage stamps, Treasury securities, identification cards, naturalization certificates, and other special security documents at its facilities in Washington, D.C., and Fort Worth, Texas. The Bureau also advises other Federal agencies on document security matters as well as processing claims for the redemption of mutilated currency. The BEP police is responsible for protecting and safeguarding its products from production through delivery.

The *U.S. Customs Service (USCS)* ensures that all goods and persons entering and exiting the United States do so in accordance with U.S. laws and regulations. The USCS uses a wide variety of spectrum-dependent equipment to accomplish its missions. The USCS operates the Customs Over-the-Horizon Enforcement Network which is designed to provide communications connectivity for air and land mobile users throughout the USP. The USCS also employs an extensive network of land mobile radio equipment to communicate among USCS personnel and between USCS personnel and other Federal, state, and local law enforcement agencies. Surveillance equipment is used to covertly monitor/intercept conversations and radar is used to track aircraft and ships trying to enter or leave the country illegally.

The *Federal Law Enforcement Training Center (FLETC)* provides quality, cost-effective training for law enforcement professionals. FLETC is a partnership of Federal law enforcement organizations and faces the increasingly complex challenge of preparing Federal law enforcement officers for a demanding and hazardous environment. FLETC has been in operation for over 30 years and, currently, about 71 Federal agencies send their agents and officers to train at the main facility in Glynco, Georgia as well as facilities in Artesia, New Mexico, and Charleston, South Carolina.

Federal agents and officers across the country put their safety at risk each day performing their varied missions. It is essential that the FLETC properly prepare its students with the top-of-the-line resources to support their efforts and ensure their safety upon graduation. FLETC instructors provide training on the installation, operation, and maintenance of the wide array of devices employed by law enforcement personnel in the field. Access to the electromagnetic spectrum is fundamental to providing the training required to perform their missions once the students begin their law enforcement assignments.

The *U.S. Internal Revenue Service (IRS) Criminal Investigative Division (IRS-CID)* enforces the criminal statutes relative to tax administration and related financial crimes, in order to encourage and achieve voluntary compliance with the Internal Revenue laws. The IRS-CID plays an active role in collecting tax on all money earned, both legal and illegal. They are responsible for the investigation and prosecution of the serious tax, currency, and money laundering offenders. Additionally, the agents pursue the assets of those offenders for criminal and tax asset forfeiture purposes.

Congress has expanded IRS-CID's statutory authority to encompass not only criminal violations of the Internal Revenue Code but also money laundering and currency reporting violations. IRS-CID agents fill a unique niche in the law enforcement community, that of Financial Investigators. These special agents' combination of accounting and law enforcement skills is essential to conducting investigations leading to the conviction of high profile criminals who commit increasingly sophisticated financial crimes.

The *U.S. Mint* is responsible for manufacturing and circulating, numismatic and bullion coins at the lowest possible cost and delivering those products in a timely and secure manner. The Mint expands U.S. markets through exceptional customer service, product development, and innovative marketing and sells numismatic and bullion products at a reasonable price and profit. The U.S. Mint Police are responsible for the protection of the Nation's stockpiles of gold bullion and other precious assets. Mint Police use wireless services to provide security over those assets entrusted to them and the facilities in which they are developed, produced and stored.

The *U.S. Secret Service (USSS)* is charged with protecting the President, Vice President, President- and Vice President-elect, Presidential candidates, former Presidents, and their immediate families. The Secret Service also protects visiting heads of foreign states and, at the direction of the President, official representatives of the United States performing special missions abroad. They also are charged with protecting the White House complex, the Treasury Building and Treasury Annex, buildings which house presidential offices, the Vice President's residence, and various foreign diplomatic missions in the Washington, D.C. metropolitan area or in other areas as designated by the President.

The Secret Service also detects and arrests persons committing offenses against the laws of the United States relating to coins, currency, stamps, Government bonds, checks, credit and debit card fraud, computer fraud, false identification crimes, and other obligations or securities of the United States. They also investigate crimes related to certain criminal violations of the Federal Deposit Insurance Act, the Federal Land Bank Act, and the Government Losses in Shipment Act.

There has been more emphasis on domestic anti- and counter-terrorism, cyber-crimes and other technology threats that the Secret Service is directly involved in combating. The Secret Service was directed to design, plan and implement security for all Major Events, as defined by the National Security Council, through Presidential Decision Directive (PDD) 62. The Secret Service established the Major Event Division which must be capable of supporting two simultaneous Major Events. Another Presidential Decision Directive, PDD 63, directs the Secret Service to work with other Federal agencies and the private sector through the National Infrastructure Protection Center to increase information sharing among organizations and to identify and put in place measures to ensure the security of the Nation's critical infrastructure.

The Secret Service's mission has become significantly more complex due to the technologically sophisticated and ever-changing world environment. Secret Service special agents, uniformed officers and technical security personnel make extensive use of wireless sensors, body microphones, surveillance transceivers, detection devices, land mobile radios, and the advanced law enforcement response technology (ALERT) mobile response vehicle program to accomplish its investigative and protective missions.

The *Treasury Inspector General for Tax Administration (TIGTA)* was created on January 18, 1999 as a result of the Internal Revenue Service Reform and Restructuring Act of 1998. Congress believed there should be one independent organization solely devoted to oversight of the IRS and directed its creation through the law. The law transferred the former IRS Inspection Service to the newly formed TIGTA. TIGTA provides leadership and coordination and recommends policy for IRS activities designed to promote economy, efficiency, and effectiveness in the administration of the internal revenue laws and prevent and detect fraud and abuse in the programs and operations of the IRS and related entities. TIGTA auditors and investigators make extensive use of wireless devices to assure the integrity of the Nation's tax and revenue programs.

Tennessee Valley Authority

The Tennessee Valley Authority is a multipurpose regional development agency involved in activities such as flood control, agriculture and environmental research, forestry, recreation, diversified industry and the largest electrical utility in the United States, with some 31,109 megawatts of power generating capacity in service and another 8,000 megawatts of capacity under construction to meet power demands in the 1980's, 27,200 kilometers of transmission line are used to serve 25 million people throughout the 205,000 square kilometer area. The Tennessee Valley Authority uses extensive microwave, land mobile, and point-to-point radio systems to aid in carrying out its responsibilities for the management and operation of a $2 billion per year multipurpose activity which is essential to the socioeconomic well being of the South.

Broadcasting Board of Governors

The Broadcasting Board of Governors (BBG) promotes understanding abroad for the United States, its policies, its people, and its culture. As the official voice of the U.S. Government, BBG plays a significant role in the achievement of long-range foreign policy objectives as it informs and explains — encouraging the maximum flow of ideas and information between the people of the United States and the people of other countries. Radio is the only means of communicating directly with peoples of other nations. BBG's global radio network, the Voice of America (VOA), consists of 107 shortwave and medium wave transmitters located in the United States and 10 foreign countries with a total transmitting power of over 22 million watts. A total of 960 hours of direct broadcast programming in 42 languages is transmitted overseas each week reaching an audience estimated to exceed 100 million listeners. All broadcasts originate from studios in Washington, D.C., and are transmitted simultaneously by microwave of leased satellite circuits to domestic relay stations operating a total of 75 transmitters, which receive all broadcast by leased satellite circuits or by shortwave from the relay stations. These broadcasts are then simultaneously rebroadcast on shortwave and medium wave frequencies to designated target areas. In addition to the direct broadcast, VOA operates a radio teletype network five days a week sending five regional transmissions of policy statements and interpretive material to over 100 BBG posts abroad.

U.S. Postal Service

The U.S. Postal Service's (USPS) beginnings can be traced back to the birth of the Nation. The Continental Congress named Benjamin Franklin as the first Postmaster General in 1775. The postal system that the Congress created was to help bind the new Nation together, support the growth of commerce and ensure a free flow of ideas and information. Public Law 91–375, signed by President Richard M. Nixon on August 12, 1970, transformed the Post Office Department into the USPS.

The new Postal Service officially began operations on July 1, 1971, at which time the Postmaster General left the President's Cabinet. The USPS now operates under a Board of Governors that approves postal rates and directs the exercise of the powers of the Postal Service. Members of the Board of Governors are appointed by the President.

The USPS operates 38,019 post offices around the country; delivers to 130 million addresses every day; handles 41 percent of the world's mail volume (630 million pieces every day); has 192,904 motor vehicles; is the Nation's largest civilian employer with more than 765,000 career employees; and has 2,990 frequency assignments.

The USPS utilizes radio communications for various purposes in order to deliver the mail to the Nation. The frequency assignments are used for mail processing activities, maintenance of property and mail processing equipment, transportation of mail, law enforcement, and maintaining the vehicle fleet.

The *Postal Inspection Service* is the law enforcement and audit arm of the USPS. Having investigated crimes involving the mails for more than 200 years, the U.S. Postal Inspection Service is one of the oldest investigative agencies of the U.S. Government. Postal Inspectors have statutory authority to serve federal warrants and subpoenas, and to make arrests for postalrelated offenses. Presently, there are more than 2,000 Postal Inspectors stationed throughout the United States.

The U.S. Postal Inspection Service has three basic responsibilities:

- Investigation of violations of over 200 Federal statutes relating to Postal Service crimes.

- Protection of mail, postal funds and property, and postal employees;

- Conducting internal audits of many Postal Service financial and non-financial operations.

The U.S. Postal Inspection Service investigates, and seeks to prevent criminal assaults against the Postal Service or its employees and misuse of the Nation's postal system. Its responsibilities include investigation of offenses such as: armed robberies; murder of, or assault upon, postal employees; burglaries; theft of mail; mailings of obscene matter, child pornography, bombs, and drugs; and use of the mails to swindle the public.

Criminal investigations cover:

- Robbery--Robbery of mail, money or other property of the Postal Service from any person having custody or control thereof.

- Burglary--The forcible breaking into and entering (or attempting to do so) of any postal facility with intent to commit larceny.

- Assaults upon and murders of officers and employees of the Postal Service while in the performance of their duties or occurring as a result of such performance.

- Theft of mail or possession of stolen mail taken from postal custody or from authorized home and apartment mail receptacles.

- Bombs and explosives sent through the mails.

- Mail fraud--Use of the mails to obtain money or property by means of false or fraudulent pretenses, representations, or promises.

- Controlled Substances--Using the mails to distribute narcotics and other illegal controlled substances.

- Unlawful sale or possession of controlled substances by postal employees while on duty or on postal property.

- Misappropriation of postal funds by postal employees.

- Fraudulent Workers' Compensation claims filed by postal employees.

- Extortion--That portion of the extortion statute concerning a mailed threat to injure an individual's reputation or to accuse the individual of a crime.

- Obscenity--Use of the mail to distribute obscene material or unsolicited sexually oriented advertisements.

- Prohibited matter in general--Mailing of poisons, switchblade knives, flammable materials and other hazardous material that can kill or injure an individual or injure the mail or other property.

- Counterfeiting of postmarks, postage stamps, postage meter stamps, postal cards, postal money orders and any dies, plates or engravings thereof. (Jurisdiction shared with U.S. Secret Service.)

- Revenue fraud against the Postal Service. Large postal mailers such as utility companies and retail stores whose operations generate high volumes of stamped mailing envelopes from their customers are potential targets of schemes which fraudulently reuse "washed" postage stamps. These "waste" envelopes are valuable to persons who may even claim to represent a charitable group. Instead of disposing or recycling this material, individuals remove the stamps, chemically "wash" the cancellation marks, and resell the end product at a discount.

- Theft of Postal Money Orders and/or the equipment used in the preparation of such orders or the fraudulent negotiation of such orders.

- Child Pornography--Use of the mails to produce and/or distribute.

- The U.S. Postal Inspection Service utilizes radio communications for investigative, protection, surveillance and other law enforcement activities to maintain the security of the mails and safety of personnel. They also conduct joint investigations with other federal law enforcement agencies.

Department of Veterans Affairs

Executive Order 5398, signed by President Herbert Hoover on July 21, 1930, established the Department of Veterans Affairs (VA). Subsequently, President George H.W. Bush created the Cabinet-level Department of Veterans Affairs. VA brings together, under a single agency, responsibility for the various veterans programs passed by Congress over the years. The VA provides many benefits including health care, education, insurance, and mortgage benefits for our military veterans, widows, parents and orphans. To provide expeditious health care, the VA has over 3,500 frequency assignments for operation of radio paging, two-way radio, wireless microphone, cardiac telemetry, emergency medical service radio nets, citizen band radio, vehicular radar, microwave transmission systems, and a HF emergency contingency radio net.

U.S. Department of State

In the conduct of foreign affairs, the U.S. Department of State (DOS) is dependent upon the continuing availability of rapid and reliable radio communications facilities that utilize the radio frequency spectrum. The Bureau of Diplomatic Security (DS) with its protective and law enforcement missions utilizes tactical radio communications networks at DOS headquarters and at 8 field offices and 14 resident agencies throughout the United States. Special operations at peace talks, the annual United Nations General Assembly in New York City, and other special events require that DS use additional facilities. DS's operations also include the special group that provides continuous security for the Secretary of State. Other networks at DOS headquarters include fire and safety, local protective service, and installation/repair of security devices.

Under Section 305(c) of the Communications Act of 1934, as amended, (47 USC 305(c)), DOS administers radio frequency authorizations for 26 foreign embassies in Washington, DC, for radio communications facilities that allow direct communications with their foreign capitals.

Chapter 3

FUTURE FEDERAL OPERATIONAL AND SPECTRUM REQUIREMENTS

FEDERAL USE OF COMMERCIAL RADIO-COMMUNICATIONS PROVIDERS

General

The Federal Government places heavy reliance on the private sector in providing telecommunications service for its own use. This means that all functions normally associated with providing the service shall be performed by the private sector. These functions include design, engineering, system management and operation, maintenance, and logistical support.

Federal requirements for commercial wireless services have been described by the Federal Wireless Policy Committee[1] (FWPC) as part of the on-going review of Federal wireless telecommunications requirements. The FWPC notes that "The Federal Government is not a single enterprise purchaser of wireless communication goods and services. Acquisition is done by many agencies each trying to support their unique missions. However, there are certain common issues and needs, some of them government unique...." The future applications of commercial wireless will be used by not only Federal civil agencies, but also by the military, as shown

---

[1] The Federal Wireless Policy Committee (FWPC) is a multi-agency committee, chaired by NTIA, to develop policy on Federal use of wireless technologies. Information in this section was taken from the FWPC document *Federal Functional Requirements for Commercial Wireless Services, Draft Revision 1.1 of March, 1999*.

by the document *Joint Vision 2010*.[2] Mobile-satellite services (MSS), as well as government-owned personal communications service (PCS) and wireless local area networks will be deployable with military warfighting units.

Functionally, Federal wireless systems will be generally characterized as Digital, Ubiquitous, Interoperable, Transparent, and Secure (DUITS). The Federal Wireless Users Forum has addressed this concept for several years. The DUITS concept will be implemented by a mix of wireless services, such as mobile satellite, PCS, wireless private branch exchange, enhanced specialized mobile radio, and cellular telephone.

It is assumed that the majority of wireless services used by Federal agencies will operate in non-government bands. However, it is anticipated that some networks may be shared between Federal and commercial owners, and might operate in non-government, shared, or government bands. Any sharing of such networks would require that the networks accommodate Federal priority access schemes, such as the Government Emergency Telecommunications Service.

It is expected that Federal agencies will look for the economies of scale that accrue to commercial service providers, and perform cost/benefit analyses to determine if commercial services will be more economical, assuming that the commercial service satisfies the operational requirements. There will also be a mix of licensed and unlicensed systems in the Federal inventory. Systems operating under the authorization of Annex K to the NTIA Manual will become more common, but will need to share with FCC Part 15 commercial/private systems.

FEDERAL SPECTRUM REQUIREMENTS FOR GOVERNMENT-OWNED SYSTEMS

Within the jurisdiction of the U.S. Government, Federal Government use of the radio frequency spectrum for telecommunications is authorized only by the Assistant Secretary for Communications and Information. In view of the limitations of the usable radio frequency spectrum, and to ensure the best possible return from that use, the Government in time of peace requires all Federal Government users to: a) justify any except an emergency request for radio frequencies prior to the assignment and use of these

---

[2] *Joint Vision 2020* was recently published and builds on the foundation and maintains the momentum established with *Joint Vision 2010*. It confirms the direction of the ongoing DOD transformation, especially in the arena of communications operations.

frequencies; b) confirm periodically the justification of continued use; c) employ up-to-date spectrum conserving techniques as a matter of normal procedure; and d) assure the ability to discontinue the functioning of any emitting radio system, including satellites, when required in the interest of communications efficiency and effectiveness.[3]

FEDERAL GOVERNMENT CURRENT AND PROJECTED SPECTRUM REQUIREMENTS

Mobile

The Federal mobile requirements include military tactical and non-tactical systems, flight test telemetry, land, maritime and aeronautical mobile for law enforcement, search and rescue, drug interdiction, emergency response, and in support of other Federal services.

Land Mobile

The Federal non-military land mobile requirements are generally accommodated in the 162–174 MHz and 406–420 MHz bands. Although these bands are primarily for Federal civil agencies, the Military Departments have allotments, and have begun a program of large-scale trunked operations. These systems are limited to non-tactical operations. The new allotment plans call for 12.5 kHz channel spacing and a mandatory move to narrowband operation by the year 2005 for the 162–174 MHz band, and 2008 for the 406–420 MHz band. New frequency assignments in the bands generally reflect the narrowband usage along with 25 kHz authorizations.

However, equipment availability has been limited for narrowband trunking operations, and funding for replacement mobile systems is a perennial problem. Frequency assignments are becoming more difficult to obtain in the metropolitan areas as the population increases and Federal services grow to meet the demand. It is expected that future requirements for nonmilitary land mobile operations can be satisfied in the current allocations, assuming that 12.5 kHz equipment becomes readily available. Growth rates

---

[3] National Telecommunications and Information Administration, Manual of Regulations and Procedures for Federal Radio Frequency Management, §2.3.6, at 2-5 (Jan 2000).

for the bands are about five percent per year. The increasing Federal use of commercial providers serves to relieve some pressure from these bands.

DOD Mobile Requirements

Other DOD mobile operations, including aeronautical, maritime, and land tactical uses, are currently conducted in the 30–88 MHz, 138–144 MHz, 225–400 MHz, and other bands as shown in Section V. The DOD projects a requirement for an additional 115 MHz of spectrum by the year 2015. Key uses for these mobile systems include combat net radios (voice and data), situational awareness (position location and reporting), and battlefield personal communications systems.

Aeronautical Mobile

Aeronautical mobile communications are used by the Federal agencies, and are generally accommodated in the 2–23 MHz, 118–137 MHz, and 225–400 MHz bands. The NTIA Spectrum Requirements Study determined that 108 kHz of Aeronautical Mobile (R) spectrum was needed, an additional 30 kHz of Aeronautical Mobile (OR) spectrum, and an additional 100 kHz of Mobile allocations to support aeronautical operations were needed.

Flight Test Telemetry

Military and commercial aircraft flight testing use the 1435–1535 MHz, 2200–2290 MHz, and 2310–2390 MHz bands. There is a growing concern for the lack of spectrum to accommodate the future flight test telemetry operations. NASA, DOD and commercial aircraft manufacturers have large investments in aeronautical flight research and flight test programs. Emerging future requirements will place significantly larger demands on the spectrum used for flight test telemetry. High-resolution digital video and the testing of unmanned aerospace vehicles will increase the demand for spectrum beyond that which can be satisfied by current allocations. It is estimated that an additional 300 MHz will be needed for future flight testing.

Paging

Several Federal agencies satisfy paging requirements in the 162–174 MHz and 406–420 MHz land mobile bands. Manufacturers are reluctant, however, to provide systems capable of narrowband (12.5 kHz) operation. Moving the paging operations out of the land mobile band may be desirable.

Maritime Mobile

The NTIA Spectrum Requirements Study concluded that between 36–60 kHz of additional HF spectrum was required for maritime mobile operations.

Fixed

All near-term Federal fixed service requirements can be satisfied under current spectrum allocations. The 42.5–43.5 GHz band, recently converted to exclusive Federal allocations, will serve as a primary band for terrestrial services to satisfy requirements that cannot be satisfied in the 37–38.6 GHz band. However, the DOD estimates that an additional 630 MHz of spectrum will be required for DOD fixed (point-to-point) systems by the year 2015. Key uses for these point-to-point systems will include area communications, data links, precision munitions, and common tactical picture.

Radio Astronomy

Most radio astronomy requirements can be satisfied under current spectrum allocations. However, the NTIA Spectrum Requirements Study concluded that 9.6 MHz of additional allocated spectrum was required. Some radio astronomy allocations were revised in the bands above 50 GHz to use bands that were more conducive for observations.

Radiolocation

Allocations for radiolocation are, in general, adequate for the near term. There may be unique applications, such as ultra-wideband systems, that cannot be accommodated by the current allocation structure. These systems will be authorized on a case-by-case basis. An NTIA report released May 2000 concluded the current allocations for radiolocation must remain intact for the next 20 years. However, research is continuing in such areas as detection of low observables, ballistic missile defense, and spaceborne systems that need spectrum in bands not presently allocated for radar. DOD projections of spectrum requirements include: 1) a heavy reliance but minimal growth in the low radar bands for critical DOD uses in space surveillance and warning, air defense, and detection of low observables; 2) a 35 percent growth in surveillance radar requirements for critical DOD uses in air surveillance and tracking, air traffic control, and air-to-air search; and

3) a 68 percent growth in radar requirements to support advanced weapons systems for critical DOD uses in missile defense, space-based radar, and target imaging.

Radionavigation

Global Positioning System

In January 1999, Vice President Gore announced a $400 million new initiative in the President's balanced budget that will modernize the GPS and will add two new civil signals to future GPS satellites, significantly enhancing the service provided to civil, commercial, and scientific users worldwide.

This initiative is only the most recent step in an ongoing public-private effort to make GPS more responsive to the needs of civilian users worldwide. National and regional GPS-based networks are now being created by governments and industry around the world to help guide everything from planes, trains, ships, and cars to tractors, snowplows, earthmovers, and mining equipment.

The second civil signal will be located at 1227.60 MHz along with the current military signal, and will be available for general use in non-safety-critical applications. The President's Budget supports implementing this new signal on the satellites scheduled for launch beginning in 2003.

Key to the overall modernization initiative was a recent decision on the frequency for a third civil signal that can meet the needs of critical safety-of-life applications such as civil aviation. The third civil signal will be located at 1176.45 MHz, within a portion of the spectrum that is allocated nationally and internationally for aeronautical radio-navigation services, and will be implemented beginning with a satellite scheduled for launch in 2005. This initiative will cost $400 million over six years. The date that new services will be available to users will depend on the actual launch dates, orbiting sufficient numbers of satellites to provide useful services, and maintaining operational capabilities. Funding difficulties, however, may delay the implementation of additional GPS signals, and present obstacles to obtaining international recognition and protection of the new civil GPS signals.

Space Services

Space Operations

The DOD has been supporting commercial space launches in the 2200–2290 MHz band. With the increase in the number of these commercial space launches, additional frequencies are required. Three of the space operations frequencies set aside for government/non-government in the 2310–2390 MHz band were lost when the FCC auctioned licenses in a portion of the band. Additional spectrum is now required, but no agency is taking the lead to define requirements and identify spectrum for this purpose.

Space Sciences

Generally, spectrum for space research is adequate for the present. There may be a need for additional space research allocations in the future. However, spectrum for space operations is very congested at space launch facilities.

Fixed- and Mobile-Satellite

Federal use of Fixed- and Mobile-Satellite systems is heavy, and is projected to increase. The 42.5–43.5 GHz band has been recently made available for possible expansion of DOD space communications operations (uplink), shared with Federal terrestrial services. A new Federal requirement for 1 GHz of downlink spectrum below 50 GHz was recently identified. Because of the difficulty of sharing Fixed-Satellite Service (FSS) and MSS operations with high-density fixed operations in the 39.5–40.0 GHz band, the United States gained allocations at the 2000 World Radiocommunication Conference (WRC–2000) for FSS in ITU Region 1, and MSS in Region 2 in the 40.5–41.0 GHz band. Federal allocations will be added to the 40.5–41.0 GHz band in the National Table. This now makes the 40–41 GHz band available for Fixed- and Mobile-Satellite operations. DOD projections conclude that: 1) an increase in spectrum requirements from 123 to 215 MHz for highly protected SATCOM systems for critical DOD uses in assured strategic and tactical connectivity, and 2) a many fold increase for wideband SATCOM for critical DOD uses in intelligence dissemination, imagery transmission, and high-speed data and networks.

Chapter 4

FEDERAL PLAN FOR ACCOMMODATING UNSUPPORTED REQUIREMENTS

SPECIFIC FREQUENCY ALLOCATIONS NEEDED

Flight Test Telemetry	Possible allocations in the 25.25–27.0 GHz band
Radiolocation	Pending the results of the radar workshop.
Radio Astronomy	See the NTIA Special Publication 94–31 for requested allocations.
Paging	[TBD]

STRATEGY FOR OBTAINING ALLOCATIONS

Inputs for International Conferences

The Federal Government develops its inputs for international radio conferences with the participation of Federal agencies in the IRAC's *Radio Conference Subcommittee (RCS)*. The RCS develops the Federal position on revisions to the international *Radio Regulations*, including changes to the international Table of Frequency Allocations. The outputs of the RCS are sent to the IRAC for approval, and then, in consultation with the Department of State, are merged with similar proposals from the FCC, and are then considered official U.S. proposals for international conferences.

Inputs for International Study Groups

The international study groups, under the Radio-communications Sector of the ITU, develop reports and recommendations regarding use of the spectrum. These documents are used to complement the Radio Regulations. NTIA and the Federal agencies contribute technical documents to the national study groups, which along with contributions from the private sector, are considered and sent to the U.S. National Committee for approval. Approved documents are forwarded to the ITU for consideration by the international study groups.

The following issues are being tracked and addressed in the national study groups:

International Mobile Telecommunications (IMT) –2000

The International Mobile Telecommunications–2000 (IMT–2000) is an advanced mobile communications concept, and is considered as a third generation wireless system. Key features of the IMT–2000 include: a high degree of commonality of design worldwide, compatibility of services within IMT–2000 and other fixed networks, and high-quality worldwide use and roaming capability for multi-media applications (e.g., video-teleconferencing and high-speed internet access). The ITU established an agenda item for the WRC–2000 which considered the "review of spectrum and regulatory issues for advanced mobile applications in the context of IMT–2000, noting that there is an urgent need to provide more spectrum for the terrestrial component of such applications and that priority should be given to terrestrial mobile needs, and adjustments to the Table of Frequency Allocations as necessary".[1]

The 1755–1850 MHz and 2500–2690 MHz bands were some of the bands that WRC–2000 considered for IMT–2000 terrestrial systems. The U.S. position for this conference was negotiated by U.S. industry and government representatives, resulting in a proposal that the United States believed could be the basis for a compromise at the conference, given the conflicting positions of many of the other administrations. The United States suggested three possible bands for IMT–2000, including the 1710–1885 MHz band (favored by the Americas) and the 2500–2690 MHz band

---

[1] *Resolution 721 (WRC–97) Agenda for the 1999 World Radiocommunication Conference*, International Telecommunication Union Radio Regulations, Volume 3, (Geneva: ITU 1998) at 319.

(favored by Europe), and the 698–960 MHz band. At the conference, the United States stated that it would study these bands domestically to (1) see if there are alternate bands to re-accommodate the existing systems, (2) determine the costs for such a relocation, (3) who would pay for relocation, and (4) how long the transition would take.

The United States proposed and the WRC–2000 adopted full regulatory flexibility, giving each administration the right to determine which of the three bands it may want to identify for IMT–2000, if it wants to do so at all. Administrations can identify these bands at any time. Also, the United States proposed to keep bands identified for IMT–2000 open to any technology that fits in the mobile service rather that specifying a technology or standard for use in the spectrum. The United States supports the development and implementation of advancing mobile telecommunications systems, such as IMT-2000, as critical components of the communications and information infrastructure of the future.

Subsequent to the WRC–2000, the Assistant Secretary of Commerce for Communications and Information, the Chairman of the FCC, and representatives of the State Department and the DOD met with White House staff to define the process by which spectrum would be identified for IMT–2000 in the United States. It was determined that studies would be performed by NTIA (on the 1755–1850 MHz band) and the FCC (on the 2500–2690 MHz band) to determine if either or both of these bands would be viable candidates for accommodation of future IMT–2000 systems. Because of the length of time required to evaluate costs for Federal systems, NTIA would issue an interim report, followed by a final report that included cost data. The 2700–2900 MHz band is also under consideration for IMT–2000, but will not be addressed until a later WRC. Therefore, NTIA and NOAA are discussing and developing a plan for the protection of the band 2700-2900 MHz. This band is a candidate band for the terrestrial component of IMT–2000. The band is used worldwide for meteorological radars and airport surveillance radars. The plan includes submission of U.S., Inter-American Telecommunications Commission, and World Meteorological Organization contributions into TG8/1 and the conference preparatory meeting regarding sharing studies and current worldwide usage in the band.

Proposed Changes to National Table of Frequency Allocations

40.5–41.0 GHz Add Federal Government *Fixed-satellite (space-to-Earth)*
Add Federal Government *Mobile-Satellite (space-to-Earth)*
Add footnote G117

Chapter 5

PLAN FOR FEDERAL USE OF THE RADIO FREQUENCY SPECTRUM

Federal use of the spectrum is guided by the National Table of Frequency Allocations and, in particular, the spectrum allocated for use by the Federal agencies. As is current practice, there is and will be a limited amount of Federal use of non-government frequency bands, as well as non-government use of Federal frequency bands. The use of shared bands will continue to require coordination between NTIA and the FCC.

The Federal agencies plan to use the spectrum for purposes documented in Part II of this Plan, in accordance with the regulations promulgated by NTIA in the *Manual of Regulations & Procedures for Federal Radio Frequency Management* (NTIA Manual). In general, the Federal Government plans to maintain current spectrum allocations as shown in the NTIA Manual, and modified by the national implementation of revisions resulting from international radio conferences, as shown in this Part. Further, the Federal Government has long-term requirements for additional spectrum allocations as detailed in Part IV. The satisfaction of Federal telecommunications requirements is heavily dependent on commercial providers, and for that reason, there is a strong Federal interest in the various rulemakings of the FCC.

The planning version of the National Table consisting of current and planned Government allocations and usage above 30 MHz can be found on the U.S. Department of Commerce, National Telecommunications and Information Administration Website: http://www.ntia.doc.gov/osmhome/LRSP/LRSP0.htm.

The planned allocations are in accordance with the Report of the IRAC's Ad Hoc Group 206, implementing IRAC-approved revisions to the

National Table as a result of the Final Acts of the 1992 World Administrative Radio Conference and the 1995 and 1997 World Radiocommunication Conferences.

Chapter 6

ACRONYMS AND ABBREVIATIONS

ACC	Air Combat Command
AC/S	C4 Assistant Chief of Staff, Command, Control, Communications, and Computers
AETC	Air Education and Training Command
AFCA	Air Force Communications Agency
AFFMA	Air Force Frequency Management Agency
AFMC	Air Force Materiel Command
AFR	Air Force Reserve
AFRC	Air Force Reserve Command
AFSOC	Air Force Special Operations Command
AFSPC	Air Force Space Command
AIA	Air Intelligence Agency
ALERT	Advanced Law Enforcement Response Technology
ALMA	Atacama Large Millimeter Array
AMC	Air Mobility Command
ANG	Air National Guard
APHIS	Animal and Plant Health Inspection Service
BATF	Bureau of Alcohol, Tobacco and Firearms
BBG	Broadcasting Board of Governors
BEP	Bureau of Engraving and Printing
BOP	Bureau of Prisons
C2	Command and Control
C2I	Command, Control, and Intelligence
C4	Command, Control, Communications and Computer
C4I	Command, Control, Communications, Computers, and Intelligence

C4ISR	Command, Control, Communications, Computers, Intelligence, Surveillance, and Reconnaissance
CAF	Combat Air Forces
C-E	Communications-Electronics
CEC	Cooperative Engagement Capability
CNO	Chief of Naval Operations
CNO N6	Director, Space Information Warfare, Command and Control, Office of the Chief of Naval Operations
CONUS	Continental United States
DCS	Defense Communications System
DEA	Drug Enforcement Administration
DHHS	Department of Health and Human Services
DISA	Defense Information Systems Agency
DOD	Department of Defense
DOE	Department of Energy
DON	Department of Navy
DOS	Department of State
DRU	Direct Reporting Unit
DS	Diplomatic Security
DSCS	Defense Satellite Communications System
DUITS	Digital, Ubiquitous, Interoperable, Transparent, and Secure
EA	Electronic Attack
EAF	Expeditionary Air Force
ECCM	Electronic Counter-Countermeasures
ECM	Electronic Countermeasures
EHF	Extra high frequency
EVA	Extra Vehicluar Activity
FAA	Federal Aviation Administration
FBI	Federal Bureau of Investigation
FCC	Federal Communications Commission
FEMA	Federal Emergency Management Agency
FLETC	Federal Law Enforcement Training Center
FOA	Field Operating Agencies
FS	Forest Service
FSS	Fixed-Satellite Service
FWPC	Federal Wireless Policy Committee
GHz	Gigahertz
GOES	Geostationary Operational Environmental Satellite
GPS	Global Positioning System

Acronyms and Abbreviations

GSA	General Services Administration
HF	High Frequency
IHS	Indian Health Service
IMT	International Mobile Telecommunications
INS	Immigration and Naturalization Service
IRAC	Interdepartment Radio Advisory Committee
IRS	Immigration and Naturalization Service
IRS-CID	Immigration and Naturalization Service-Criminal Investigative Division
ITU	International Telecommunication Union
IT21	Information Technology for the 21st Century
kHz	Kilohertz
MAJCOM	Major Command
MHz	Megahertz
MSS	Mobile-Satellite Service
NAIC	National Atmosphere and Ionosphere Center
NAS	National Airspace System
NASA	National Aeronautics And Space Administration
NATO	North Atlantic Treaty Organization
NAVAIRSYSCOM	Naval Air Systems Command
NAVEMSCEN	Naval Electromagnetic Spectrum Center
NAVSEASYSCOM	Naval Sea Systems Command
NCAR	National Center for Atmospheric Research
NCW	Network Centric Warfare
NEMS	National Emergency Management System
NESDIS	National Environmental Satellite, Data, and Information Service
NIH	National Institute of Health
NIST	National Institute of Standards and Technology
NMFS	National Marine Fisheries Service
NOAA	National Oceanic and Atmospheric Administration
NOAO	National Optical Astronomy Observatories
NOS	National Ocean Service
NRAO	National Radio Astronomy Observatory
NRCS	Natural Resources Conservation Service
NSF	National Science Foundation
NTC	National Training Center

NTIA	National Telecommunications and Information Administration
NTS	Naval Telecommunications System
NWS	National Weather Service
(OR)	Off Route
OMFTS	Operational Maneuver From the Sea
OPNAV	Office of the Chief of Naval Operations
PACAF	Pacific Air Force
PCS	Personal Communications Service
PD	Program Directorate
PDD	Presidential Decision Directive
PEO	Program Executive Office
PHS	Public Health Service
(R)	Route
RCS	Radio Conference Subcommittee
RF	Radio Frequency
SARSAT	Search And Rescue Satellite
SHF	Super High Frequency
SPAWARSYSCOM	Space and Naval Warfare Systems Command
SYSCOMS	Systems
TDRSS	Tracking and Data Relay Satellites
TIGTA	Treasury Inspector General for Tax Administration
TT&C	Tracking, Telemetry and Command
UHF	Ultra High Frequency
USAF	U.S. Air Force
USAFE	U.S. Air Forces in Europe
USCENTCOM	U.S. Central Command
USCG	U.S. Coast Guard
USCS	U.S. Customs Service
USDA	U.S. Department of Agriculture
USJFC	U.S. Joint Forces Command
USMS	U.S. Marshals Service
USP	U.S. and its Possessions
USPS	U.S. Postal Service
USSOUTHCOM	U.S. Southern Command
USSS	U.S. Secret Service
USSTRATCOM	U.S. Strategic Command
VA	Department of Veterans Affairs
VHF	Very High Frequency

VLA	Very Large Array
VLBA	Very Long Baseline Array
VOA	Voice of America
WRC	World Radio-communication Conference

INDEX

A

academic and technical research, xii
access control, 35
acquisition, 8, 16, 17, 18, 21
adequate safety, 2
administrative procedures, vii, ix
administrative system, xii
advanced law enforcement response technology (ALERT), 46, 67
advanced television (ATV), x
aerial tankers, 22
aerial vehicles, 17, 24, 27
aerospace forces, 21
Africa, 23, 24
Air Combat Command (ACC), 19, 20, 26, 67
air defense, 57
Air Education and Training Command (AETC), 20, 21, 26, 67
Air Force Communications Agency (AFCA), 19, 25, 67
Air Force Frequency Management Agency (AFFMA), 19, 25, 26, 67
Air Force Materiel Command (AFMC), 21, 67
Air Force Reserve (AFR), 20, 23, 67
Air Force Reserve Command (AFRC), 23, 67
Air Force Space Command (AFSPC), 19, 21, 22, 67
Air Force Special Operations Command (AFSOC), 19, 20, 22, 26, 67
Air Force, 19-23, 25-27, 67
Air Intelligence Agency (AIA), 19, 24, 25, 67
Air Mobility Command (AMC), 22, 23, 26, 67
Air Mobility Operations Groups, 23
Air National Guard (ANG), 19, 20, 26, 27, 67
air traffic control, vii, xviii, 6, 7, 12, 20, 21, 23, 24, 27, 41, 57
aircraft, 7, 17, 19, 20, 22-24, 27-30, 41, 42, 44, 56
American Red Cross, xv
amphibious training exercises, 14
Animal and Plant Health Inspection Service (APHIS), 28, 67
Antarctic, 23
armed robberies, 48
Army frequency management, 12
Army National Guard, 27
Army operations, 11, 12
Army Spectrum Manager, 11
Atacama Large Millimeter Array (ALMA), 40, 67
aviation weapons, 17

B

balanced budget, 58
Ballistic Missile Warning System, 21
bank robbery, 37
best interest of the Nation, 1, 3
bombs, 20, 36, 43, 48
border patrol, 37
broadband capabilities, xvii
Broadcasting Board of Governors (BBG), 46, 67
broadcasting, vii, ix, x, xiv, xviii, 6
Bureau of Alcohol, Tobacco and Firearms (BATF), 43, 67
Bureau of Diplomatic Security (DS), 50, 68
Bureau of Engraving and Printing (BEP), 43, 67
Bureau of Indian Affairs, 36
Bureau of Land Management, 36
burglaries, 48
Bush, President George H.W., 50

C

Canada, xiv, 30
cellular radio services, ix
cellular telephony, vii
cellular-based, xvi
certified spectrum availability, xvi
Chief of Naval Operations (CNO), 15, 16, 68
child pornography, 48, 49
civil works, 12
civilian personnel, 20
coast guard, 27
Cobra Dane radar, 21
Cold War, 13
Combat Air Forces (CAF), 19, 68
combat commanders, 24
combat superiority, 21
combat-ready team, 27
Command and Control (C2), 14, 15, 23, 67, 68
command, control, communications, and computer (C4), 16, 25, 67
Command, Control, Communications, Computers and Intelligence, 16
command, control, communications, computers, and intelligence (C4I), 14, 16, 67
commercial communication, 30
commercial service(s), 3, 6, 54
communication, x, xiv-xvii, 2-4, 6-8, 11, 15, 20, 22, 30, 31, 36, 42, 53, 59, 66, 71
Communications Act, xi, xiii, 9, 50
communications systems, 38
communications, vii, ix-xiii, xvi-xviii, 2, 5, 6, 8, 10-16, 20-30, 35, 36, 38, 41-43, 47, 50, 51, 53-57, 59, 62, 63
communications-electronics (C-E), 10, 14, 28, 42, 68
Communications-Electronics Service Office, 11
computer automation process, xv
computer fraud, 45
computers, intelligence, surveillance and reconnaissance (C4ISR), 13-15, 18, 68
conservation, 2, 28, 30, 36
contamination, 30
Continental United States (CONUS), 11, 19, 24, 40, 68
continuing education, 20
control systems, xvi, 20
controlled substances, 49
conventional weapons, 14
Cooperative Engagement Capability (CEC), 14, 68
Corps of Engineers, 12, 13
counterfeiting, 42
countermeasures, 20, 24
counter-terrorism, xv, 45
crime detection, 37
crime prevention, 1, 37, 38

Index

Criminal Investigative Division (IRS-CID, 44, 69
criminals, 37, 44
cyber-crimes, 45

D

data collection, 25, 27, 29
data transmissions, 33
Defense Communications System (DCS), 11, 68
Defense Information Systems Agency (DISA), 11, 68
Defense Satellite Communications System (DSCS), 11, 21, 68
defense, vii, xiii, xv, xviii, 1, 10, 14, 19-23, 26, 31, 33, 41, 57
Department of Agriculture (USDA), 28, 70
Department of Commerce, ix, xv, xvi, 9, 29, 65
Department of Defense (DOD), xv, xvi, xviii, 11, 16, 17, 22, 25, 26, 54, 56, 57, 59, 63, 68
Department of Energy (DOE), 25, 31, 32, 33, 34, 68
Department of Health and Human Services (DHHS), 35, 36, 68
Department of Justice, xv, 37, 38
Department of State (DOS), xiii, 50, 61, 68
Department of the Army, 11
Department of the Navy (DON), 13, 15, 16, 18, 68
Department of Veterans Affairs (VA), 50, 70
deportation, 37
depressants, 38
development complex, 7
digital audio broadcasting, x
digital video, 56
Digital, Ubiquitous, Interoperable, Transparent, and Secure (DUITS), 54, 68

diplomatic security, 68
Direct Reporting Unit(s) (DRU(s)), 19, 68
distance measurements, 30
distress signals, 30
drug abuse, 37
Drug Enforcement Administration (DEA), 37, 68
drug traffickers, 38, 43

E

Earth observation, 7
Earth terminals, 11
earthquakes, 28, 36
economic activity, 41
economic and social development, ix
economic equations, 8
economy, vii, 3, 4, 6, 29, 31, 46
efficiency, 3, 4, 10, 31, 33, 46, 55
electric power, 13
electrical power supply systems, 33
electricity, 32
Electronic Attack (EA), 27, 68
electronic combat, 24
electronic counter-countermeasures (ECCM), 27, 68
electronic countermeasures (ECM), 27, 68
electronic devices, 6
electronic facilities, 6
electronic proving grounds, 11
electronic warfare, 15, 17, 20, 24
embedded automation, 12
emergency disaster control, 28
emergency preparedness, 34
emergency request, 4, 54
enemy threat simulators, 20, 24
energy (re)sources, 31, 32
energy supply, 32
energy technologies, 32
engineering, xi, 10, 17, 18, 31, 32, 53
environmental protection, 42
espionage, 37

excess weapons, 31
exclusion, 37
Expeditionary Air Force (EAF), 20, 68
explosives, 43, 48
extortion, 37, 49
extra high frequency (EHF), 11, 12, 68

F

federal agencies, xiii-xviii, 4, 8, 11, 40, 43-45, 54, 56, 61, 62, 65
Federal Aviation Administration (FAA), 41, 68
Federal Bureau of Investigation (FBI), 37, 68
Federal Bureau of Prisons (BOP), 38, 67
Federal Communications Commission (FCC), vii, x-xiv, xvi-xviii, 9, 11, 54, 59, 61, 63, 65, 68
Federal Deposit Insurance Act, 45
Federal Emergency Management Agency (FEMA), xv, 34, 68
federal government, vii, x-xii, xiv, 3-7, 9, 31, 34, 53-55, 61, 64, 65
Federal Land Bank Act, 45
Federal Law Enforcement Training Center (FLETC), 44, 68
Federal prisoners, 38
federal spectrum, vii, xii
Federal telecommunications systems, 3
Federal Wireless Policy Committee (FWPC), 53, 68
fiber optic cables, 11
Field Operating Agencies (FOAs), 19, 24, 68
Fixed-Satellite Service (FSS), 59, 68
Flight Test Telemetry, 56, 61
flying training, 20
force projection, 15

foreign affairs, 1, 50
Forest Service (FS), 28, 68
forgery, 42
France, 30
Franklin, Benjamin, 47
fraud, 42, 45, 46, 49
frequency assignments, xiii, xv, xvi, 11, 16, 21, 26, 35, 37, 40, 47, 50, 55
fresh water systems, 35

G

General Services Administration (GSA), 35, 69
geological survey, 36
Geostationary Operational Environmental Satellite (GOES), 29, 31, 68
gigahertz (GHz), xiv, 24, 31, 34, 57, 59, 61, 64, 68
global markets, xvii
global non-proliferation, 32
global positioning satellite (GPS), xviii, 21, 31, 42, 58, 68
Global Positioning System, 21, 58, 68
Gore, Vice President, 58
Government Emergency Telecommunications Service, 54
government functions, vii
Government Losses in Shipment Act, 45
government radio facilities, 7
government-owned radio stations, x
growth and economy, 1, 36
Gulf Coast, 33
gun law violations, 43
gunships, 22

H

hazardous chemical spills, 30
hazardous material, 49

Index

health care, 35, 50
high frequency (HF), 7, 11, 16, 20, 21, 23, 24, 26, 30, 34, 35, 50, 57, 69
higher frequenc(y)ies, x, xiv
high-resolution, 56
Hoover, Commerce Secretary Herbert, xi
host nation, 11
HQ Air Force Communications and Information Center, 19
human intelligence, 24
hurricanes, 28, 29, 36

I

illegal controlled substances, 49
illegal drug traffic, 19
illegal trafficking, 38
Immigration and Naturalization Service (INS), 37, 69
increasing demand, x
Indian Health Service (IHS), 35, 69
inflexible regulation, vii, ix
information superiority, 13
Information Technology for the 21st Century (IT21), 14, 69
Information transfer systems, 18
infrared spectrums, 30
inmates, 38
innovation, vii, ix
Integrated Emergency Management System, 34
intelligence, 13, 15, 24, 25, 59
Interdepartment Radio Advisory Committee (IRAC), xiv, 9, 26, 61, 65, 69
interference, x, xvi, xviii, 12, 15
Intergovernmental Maritime Consultative Organization, 3
internal audits, 48
Internal Revenue Service (IRS), 44, 46, 69

International Civil Aviation Organization, 3
International Mobile Telecommunications (IMT), xvii, 62, 63, 69
International Mobile Telecommunications-2000 (IMT-2000), xvii, 63
international relations, 2
International Telecommunication Union (ITU), xvii, 3, 12, 16, 26, 59, 62, 69
international treaty obligations, 1
international treaty, xiii, 1
intrusion detection, 35
inventory control, 7
investigation, xv, 2, 44, 48
investment, 3, 6, 34, 35, 39-42

J

Joint Chiefs of Staff, 10, 15
Joint Spectrum Center, xvi
Joint Strike Fighter (JSF), 17
Joint Surveillance System, 20
Joint Surveillance Target Attack Radar System, 20
Joint Tactical Information Distribution System, 20, 24

K

kidnapping, 37

L

land lines, 11
land mobile, 7, 20, 21, 23, 24, 27, 31, 34, 37, 38, 43, 45, 46, 55, 56
land vehicles, 27
laser frequencies, 11
law enforcement organizations, 38, 44

law enforcement, xiii, xv, 1, 6, 7, 28, 35-38, 42-44, 48, 50, 55
life cycle, 17, 18, 21
location information, 30
logistical support, 36, 53
long-range navigation (LORAN), 42
long-range, 7, 13, 46
low frequencies, x
low frequency ranges, xiv
low-powered devices, 7

M

maintenance, xiii, 11, 17, 32, 36, 44, 47, 53
Major Commands (MAJCOMs), 19, 26
Major Systems Commands (SYSCOMS), 17, 70
management systems, 18
managing spectrum, x
manufacturing, vii, 32, 44
marijuana, 38
marine corps, 13, 14, 16, 18, 26, 27
marine navigation, 2
marine resources, 29, 30
maritime power projection, 14
means of communication, 1, 2, 3
medical radio communications frequencies, 35
Megahertz (MHz), xv, xvii, 24, 29, 55-59, 62, 63, 65, 69
Mexico, xiv, 39, 40, 44
microwave point-to-point communication facilities, 7
microwave radio relay systems, 13
Middle East, 24
Military C-E systems, 10
military operational needs, 13
military, ix, 5, 7, 10, 13, 15, 20, 21, 24, 26, 41, 42, 50, 53, 55, 58
missile detection, 7
mission requirements, 4, 20
mobile devices, 7

mobile radio systems, 20, 24, 27
Mobile-Satellite Service, 69
Mobile-satellite services (MSS), 54, 59, 69
mobility, 8, 12, 14, 19
mobilization readiness, 23, 28
modernization, 12, 17, 58
modulation equipment, 12
moonshining, 43
multiple bands, xvii

N

narcotics, 22, 49
narrowband, 55, 56
National Aeronautics and Space Administration (NASA), 39, 56, 69
National Airborne Operations Center, 20
National Airspace System (NAS), 41, 69
National and International Radio Regulations, 10
National Atmosphere and Ionosphere Center (NAIC), 39, 40, 69
National Center for Atmospheric Research (NCAR), 39, 40, 69
national disasters, xiii
national emergencies, xv, 34
National Emergency Management System (NEMS), 34, 69
national goals, xii, 1
National Institute of Health (NIH), 35, 69
National Institute of Standards and Technology (NIST), 31, 69
national interest, xi, 2, 3
National Marine Fisheries Service (NMFS), 30, 69
national objectives, 1
National Ocean Service (NOS), 30, 69

Index

National Oceanic and Atmospheric Administration (NOAA), 29, 30, 63, 69
National Optical Astronomy Observatories (NOAO), 39, 69
National Park Service, 36
national policy, 15
National Radio Astronomy Observatory (NRAO), 39, 40, 69
national resources, 2
National Science Foundation (NSF), 39, 40, 69
National Security, 31, 45
National Table of Frequency Allocations, 9, 65
National Telecommunications and Information Administration (NTIA), vii, x-xviii, 7, 9, 53-57, 61-63, 65, 69
National Training Centers (NTC), 12, 69
National Weather Service (NWS), 29, 70
National Wildlife Refuge, 36
Native Americans, 35
natural resources, xiii, 2, 36
naturalization, 37, 43
Naval Air Systems Command (NAVAIRSYSCOM), 17, 18, 69
Naval Electromagnetic Spectrum Center (NAVEMSCEN), 16, 69
naval forces, 14
Naval Sea Systems Command (NAVSEASYSCOM), 17, 69
naval warfare, 13
Navy and Marine Corps, 13-17
Navy, 13-18, 26, 27, 30, 68
Network Centric Warfare (NCW), 14, 15, 69
Nixon, President Richard M., 47
non-commercial approach, 3
non-Government radio operations, 7
non-military telecommunications, 5
non-tactical operations, 55

North American Aerospace Defense Command, 19
North Atlantic Treaty Organization (NATO), 22, 24, 69
nuclear dangers, 32
nuclear detonation detection, 7
nuclear testing, 31

O

obscenity, 49
offensive and defensive operations, 13
Office of Emergency Preparedness, 36
Office of Management and Budget (OMB), 3
Office of the Chief of Naval Operations (OPNAV), 13, 15, 68, 70
off-shore oil fields, 36
Omnibus Budget Reconciliation Act, xv
operating budgets, 6
Operation Desert Storm, 36
Operational Maneuver from the Sea (OMFTS), 14, 15, 70
operational requirements, 4, 34, 54
operational standpoint, 3
OpNav, 15
overseas, 17, 19, 47

P

Pacific Air Force (PACAF), 19, 23, 24, 26, 70
paid advertising, xi
Passive Space Surveillance System, 22
peace(time), xiii, xv, 4, 10, 15, 23, 28, 34, 50, 54
Pentagon, xv
performance criterion, 4

personal communications services (PCS), x, xvii, 54, 70
personal communications systems, 56
physical properties, 7
policy adviser, xiii
politicians, xi
position locating, 7
postage stamps, 43, 49
postal funds, 48, 49
Postal Inspection Service, 48, 50
Postal Money Orders, 49
Postal Service, 47, 48, 49
powerful influence, 1
Presidential Decision Directive (PDD), 45, 70
private sector, x, xii-xv, xviii, 3, 6, 8, 9, 33, 45, 53, 62
privately-owned and operated radio-based services, xi
productivity, vii, 31, 32, 34
Program Directorates (PD), 18, 70
Program Executive Office(s) (PEO(s)), 17, 70
property, 1, 2, 29, 35, 36, 38, 43, 47-49
prosecution, 37, 44
Protection of mail, 48
psychological operations, 22
public domain, 3
Public Health Service (PHS), 35, 36, 70
public outreach, xvii
public response, xi
public safety, vii, xiii, xv, 36
Puerto Rico, 26

R

radar(s), xvi, xvii, 7, 12, 14, 20-22, 24, 27, 29, 34, 40, 41, 44, 50, 57, 61, 63
Radio Act of 1927, 9
radio astronomy, 39, 57, 61, 69
radio base stations, 35
radio broadcasters, x
radio communications equipment, ix
radio communications networks, 50
Radio Conference Subcommittee (RCS), 61, 70
radio equipment, ix, 28, 30, 44
radio frequenc(y)ies (RF), xiii, 3, 4, 6, 7, 9-14, 16, 19-22, 24-30, 35-37, 40, 41, 50, 54, 70
radio interference, x
radio regulations, 61, 62
radio services, xvi, 8, 21
radio spectrum, 1, 2, 4, 12, 29, 31, 35, 39-42
radio systems, 7, 9, 28, 34, 35, 38, 46
radio transmissions, 3
radio-communication services, xiv, 2, 7
radio-communications, vii, 6, 7, 30
radiolocation, xvi, 57, 61
radio-navigation, xvi, 7, 41
radio-related technologies, ix
reconnaissance, 15, 19, 22, 29
regulatory strategies, xii
rehabilitation, 37
relay of signals, 7
remote control, 7, 42
research and development activities, 2
resource management, 11
revised strategy, 13
Russia, 30

S

sabotage, 37
satellite frequency assignments, 16, 26
satellite initiatives, 42
satellite links, 24
satellite-based mobile services, x
satellite-borne data communications, 5

satellites, xviii, 4, 11, 20, 21, 29-31, 34, 39, 55, 58
savings, 3, 32
Search And Rescue Satellite (SARSAT), 30, 70
search and rescue, xv, 20, 42, 55
Secret Service, 45
security, 1, 2, 4, 7, 10, 20, 23, 24, 28, 31, 36-38, 42, 43, 45, 50
September 11th, xv
service industries, vii
signal processing techniques, 12
single sideband, 20, 24
smuggling, 42, 43
socioeconomic, 46
software-defined radios, 12
Space and Naval Warfare Systems Command
space sensors, 18
SPAWAR, 18, 19
SPAWARSYSCOM, 18
SPAWARSYSCOM, 18, 70
spectrum conserving techniques, 4, 55
spectrum efficiency, xiii
spectrum interests, xiii
spectrum management forums, 11
spectrum management policies, vii, ix
spectrum management, vii, ix-xiv, xvi, xviii, 9, 11, 16, 25, 26
spectrum managers, x, 8
spectrum requirements, xiii, xv, xvii, 8, 10, 28, 57, 59
spectrum resource, vii, ix, 8
spectrum use and management, xi
spectrum-conserving methods, 4
Spectrum-conserving systems, 4
spectrum-dependent equipment, 6, 11, 43
spectrum-dependent radio-communication systems, 6
spectrum-dependent systems, 7, 8, 12
spread-spectrum modulation, 8

standardization, 2
stimulants, 38
stolen mail, 48
Strategic Petroleum Reserve program, 33
subversion, 37
subversive activities, 37
super high frequency (SHF), 23, 70
support units, 12
surveillance, 13, 14, 15, 20, 27, 34, 41, 45, 50, 57, 63

T

Tactical Aircraft Programs, 17
tactical and strategic operations, 10
tactical radio relay systems, 12
tactical systems, 12, 15, 55
tax evasion, 43
technical intelligence, 24
technical training, 20
technological developments, xiii
technology, ix-xi, xvii, 4, 13, 15, 21, 24, 27, 31, 32, 34, 39, 45, 63
telecommunications, vii, xii, xiii, 3, 5, 6, 9, 10, 33, 34, 39, 53, 54, 63, 65
telemetry, 7, 22, 27, 29, 31, 34, 36, 40, 50, 55, 56
terrestrial, xvi, xvii, 7, 18, 21, 36, 39, 57, 59, 62, 63
terrorist attacks, xv
test and evaluation, 18
theft of mail, 48
third generation (3G), xiv, xvii, 62
Tracking and Data Relay Satellites (TDRSS), 39, 70
training, 10-12, 14, 17, 20, 21, 23, 24, 27, 28, 44
transmitted data, 30
transportation, 2, 32, 41, 48
Treasury Inspector General for Tax Administration (TIGTA), 46, 70
treaty monitoring, 24

TV and radio broadcasting, xviii

U

U.S. Air Force (USAF), 19, 21, 22, 70
U.S. Air Forces in Europe (USAFE), 19, 24, 70
U.S. Central Command (USCENTCOM), 19, 70
U.S. Coast Guard (USCG), 13, 30, 42, 70
U.S. Customs Service (USCS), 43, 70
U.S. Department of the Treasury, 42, 43
U.S. Joint Forces Command (USJFC), 19, 70
U.S. Marshals Service (USMS), 38, 70
U.S. Postal Service (USPS), 47, 48, 70
U.S. Secret Service (USSS), 45, 49, 70
U.S. Southern Command (USSOUTHCOM), 19, 70
U.S. Strategic Command (USSTRATCOM), 19, 70
U.S. Transportation Command, 19, 22
ultra high frequency (UHF), 12, 20, 21, 23-25, 27, 29, 70
ultrawideband (UWB), xvii, xviii
United States and its Possessions (USP), 14, 23, 26, 43, 70
usable radio spectrum, xiv

V

very high frequency (VHF), 12, 20, 21, 23, 24, 27, 30, 70

Very Large Array (VLA), 40, 71
Very Long Baseline Array (VLBA), 40, 71
Virgin Islands, 26, 40
Voice of America (VOA), 47, 71

W

war(fare), 10, 13, 15, 18, 22, 23, 25, 26, 28
warfighter(s), 13, 16, 20, 22
warfighting, 13, 21, 54
warning control system, xvi
weapon systems, 15, 20, 27
weapons control, 7
weapons, 7, 12, 15, 17, 18, 26, 27, 31, 58
weather forecasting, vii
weather observation, 7
weather surveillance, 42
White House Communications Agency, xv
White Sands Missile Range, 11
wildfire firefighting, 28
wireless communications, x
wireless services, xvii, 43, 45, 53, 54
wireless systems, xvii, 54
wireless telecommunications, xvi, 53
World Meteorological Organization, 3, 29, 63
World Radio-communication Conference (WRC-2000), xvii, 59, 62, 63, 71
world resource, 3
World Trade Center, xv
worldwide operations, 20
worldwide, xvi, 2, 5, 11, 14, 16, 20, 22, 25, 26, 28, 30, 58, 62, 63